The Beatles / 1967-1970

Exclusive Distributors:
Music Sales Limited
8/9 Frith Street,
London W1V 5TZ, England.
Music Sales Pty Limited
120 Rothschild Avenue,
Rosebery, NSW 2018,
Australia.

Order No.NO90611
ISBN 0-7119-5016-4
This book © Copyright 1995 by Wise Publications

Music Sales' complete catalogue describes thousands of titles and is available
in full colour sections by subject, direct from Music Sales Limited.
Please state your areas of interest and send a cheque/postal order for £1.50 for postage to:
Music Sales Limited, Newmarket Road, Bury St. Edmunds, Suffolk IP33 3YB.

Wise Publications
London/New York/Paris/Sydney/Copenhagen/Madrid

Strawberry Fields Forever

Words and Music by John Lennon and Paul McCartney

* This song is a compilation of two takes, one in the key of A (the first minute of the song) and another in the key of B♭ (the remainder). The difference in keys was compensated for by speeding up the first take and slowing down the second, though this match is not exact.

** Mellotron arr. for gtr.

* Gtr. 2 (clean elec.)

let ring throughout
w/ pick and fingers

* tuned down 1 1/2 steps: ⑥ = C♯ ⑤ = F♯ ④ = B ③ = E ② = G♯ ① = C♯
Music notated in sounding pitches.

Fill 1
* Gtr. 3 (clean elec.)

w/ slide

* Gtr. 3 tuned down 1/2 steps: ⑥ = C♯ ⑤ = F♯ ④ = B ③ = E ② = G♯ ① = C♯
Music notated in sounding pitches.

Gtr. 1 tacet

* At this point all gtrs. are arr. to remain in the Key of A

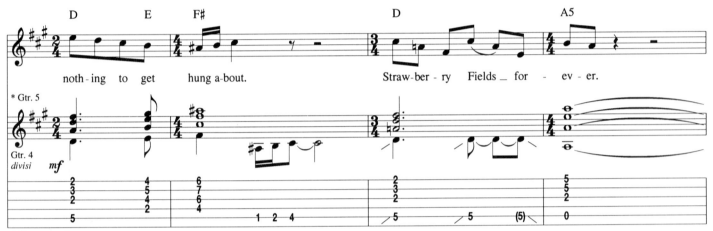

* Horns arr. for gtr.

Verse

Gtr. 6: w/ Fill 2

Gtr. 4 tacet

Fill 2

* Gtr. 6 (swordmandel arr. for gtr.)

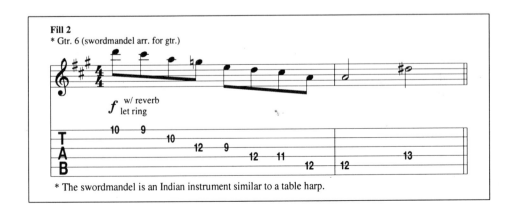

* The swordmandel is an Indian instrument similar to a table harp.

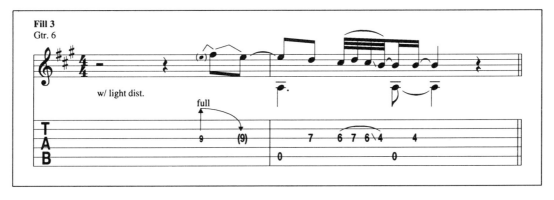

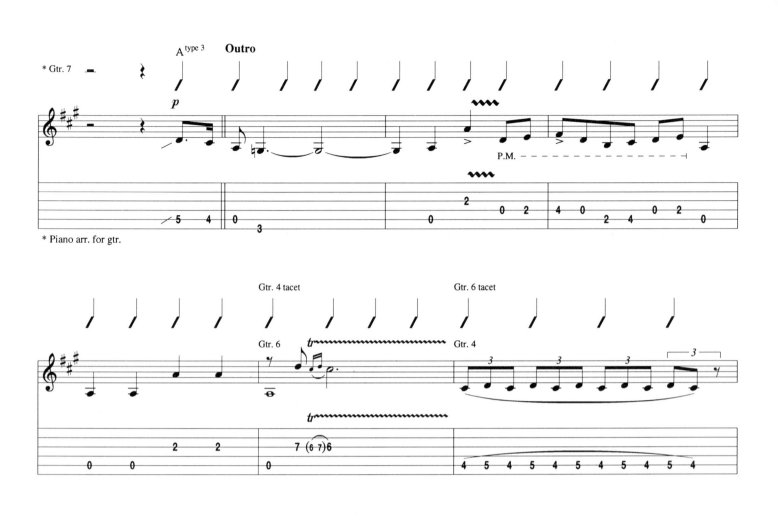

* Gtr. 7

A^type 3 **Outro**

* Piano arr. for gtr.

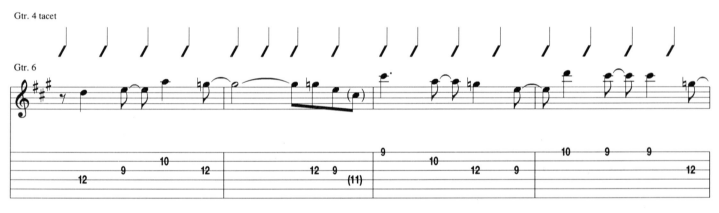

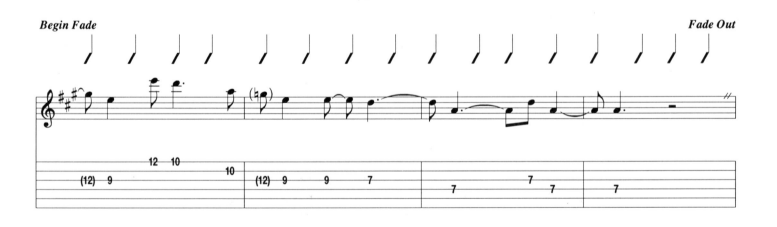

Penny Lane

Words and Music by John Lennon and Paul McCartney

Sgt. Pepper's Lonely Hearts Club Band

Words and Music by John Lennon and Paul McCartney

1. It was twen-ty years a-go to-day, Ser-geant Pep-per taught the band to play. They've been go-ing in and out of style, but they're

guar-an-teed to raise a smile. _____ So may I in-tro-duce to you _____ the

act you've known for all these years? _____ Ser - geant Pep-per's Lone - ly Hearts_ Club Band. _

Interlude

Gtrs. 1, 2, & 3 tacet

We're

* Gtr. 4

* Gtr. 5

* French horn arr. for gtr.

Gtr. 2

18

With A Little Help From My Friends

Words and Music by John Lennon and Paul McCartney

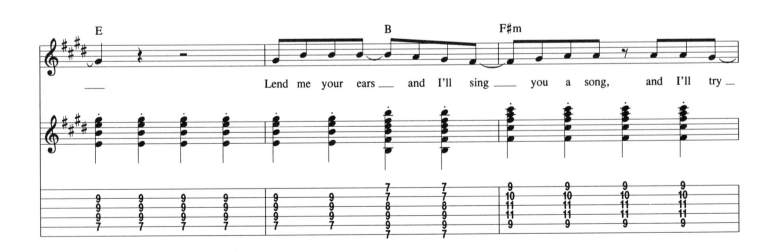

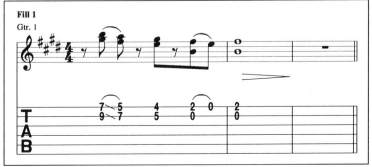

Lucy In The Sky With Diamonds

Words and Music by John Lennon and Paul McCartney

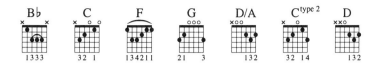

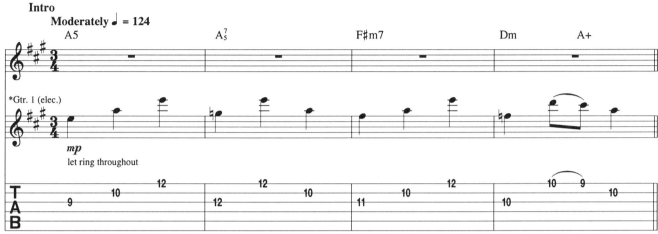

* Hammond organ arr. for gtr.

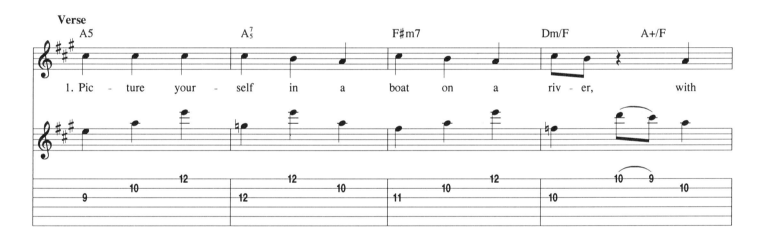

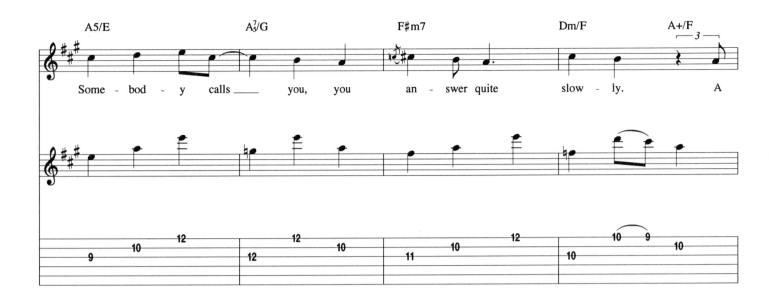

Some - bod - y calls _____ you, you an - swer quite slow - ly. A

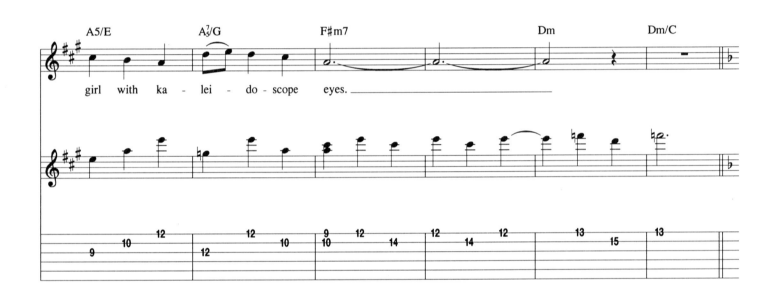

girl with ka - lei - do - scope eyes. _____

Pre-Chorus

Cel - lo - phane _____ flow - ers of yel - low and green

dia - monds.   Lu - cy in the sky __ with dia - monds,   ah. _____

Verse

2. Fol - low her down to a bridge __ by a foun - tain where

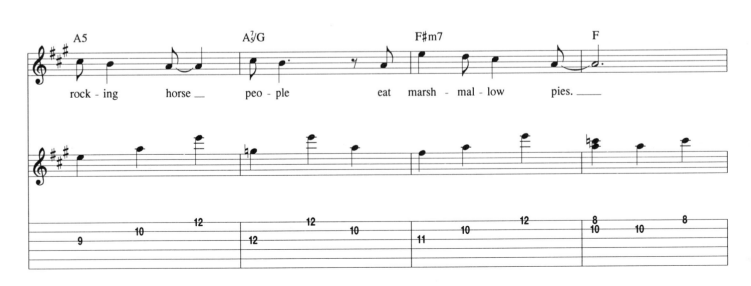

rock - ing horse __ peo - ple eat marsh - mal - low pies. ____

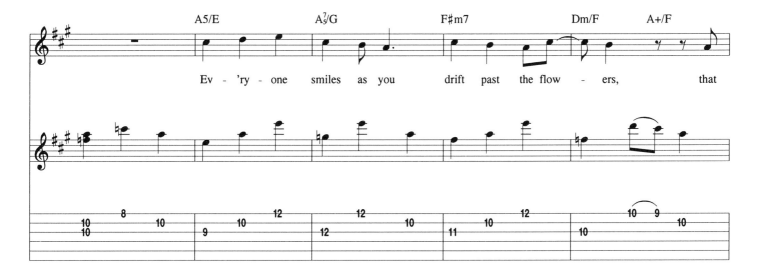

Ev-'ry-one smiles as you drift past the flow - ers, that

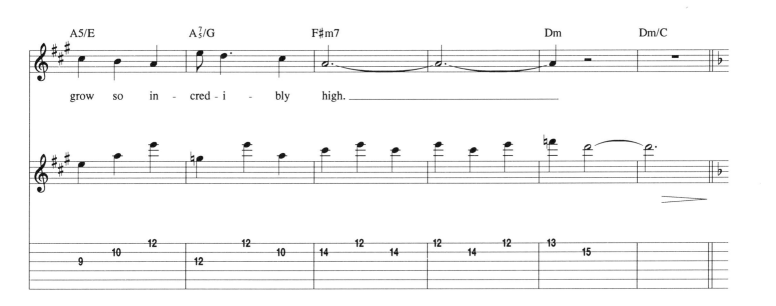

grow so in - cred - i - bly high. _____

Pre-Chorus
Gtr. 1 tacet

News - pa - per tax - is ap - pear _____ on the shore, _____

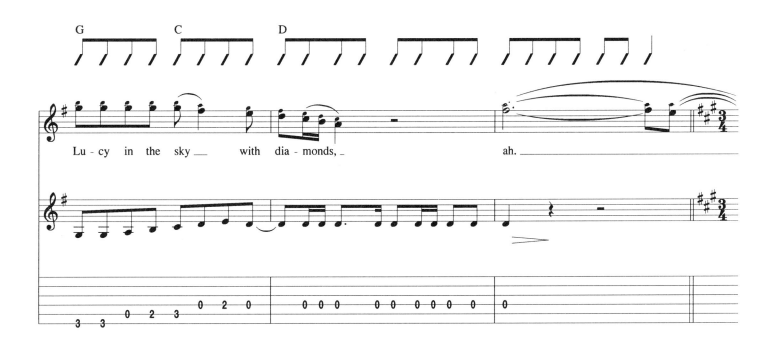

Lu - cy in the sky __ with dia - monds, __ ah. __

Verse

♩ = ♩

Gtrs. 2 & 3 tacet

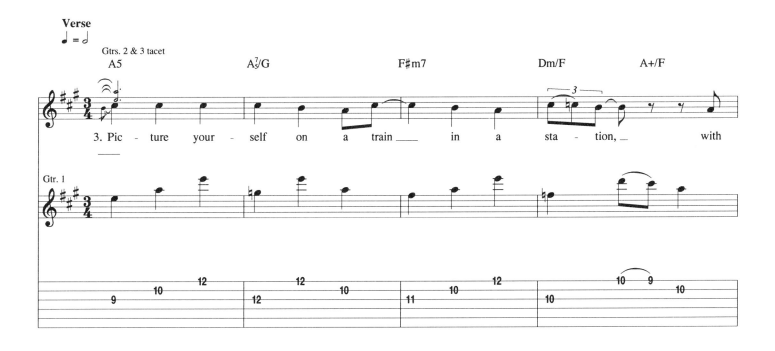

3. Pic - ture your - self on a train __ in a sta - tion, __ with

Gtr. 1

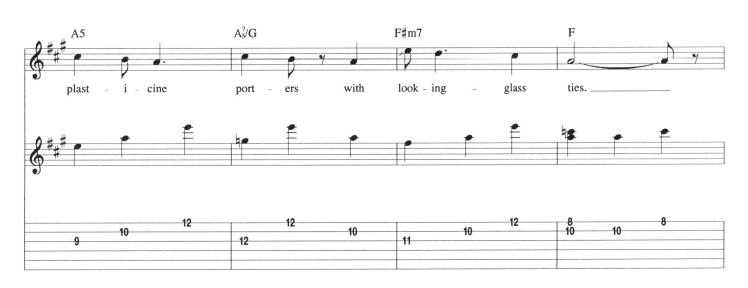

plast - i - cine port - ers with look - ing - glass ties. __

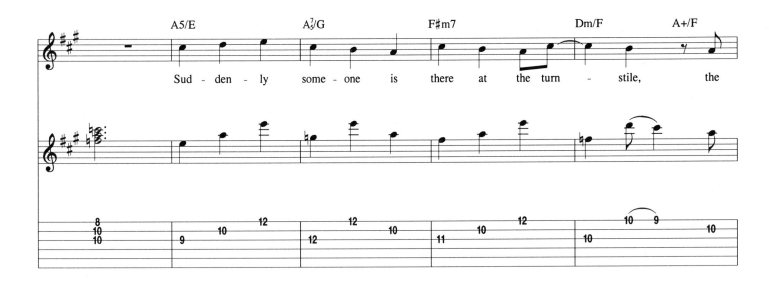

Sud- den- ly some- one is there at the turn- stile, the

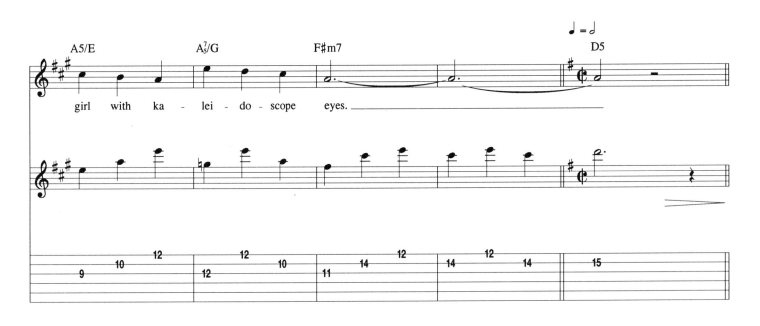

girl with ka- lei- do- scope eyes. _____

Chorus

Gtr. 1 tacet

Gtr. 2
w/ flanging

Lu- cy in the sky __ with dia- monds.   Lu- cy in the sky __ with dia- monds. __

Gtr. 3

f w/ Leslie

A Day In The Life

Words and Music by John Lennon and Paul McCartney

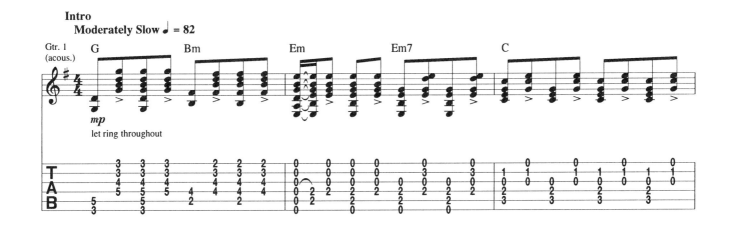

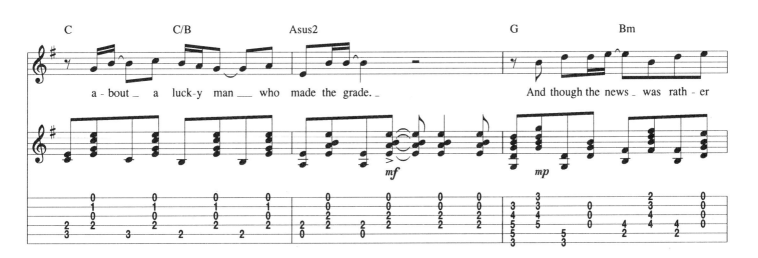

Verse
Double-Time ♩ = 164

ah,

ah.

ah.

4. I read the news ___ to - day, ___ oh boy.

Four thou - sand holes ___ in Black - burn, Lan - ca - shire. ___

And though the holes ___ were rath - er

Gtr. 1

All You Need Is Love

Words and Music by John Lennon and Paul McCartney

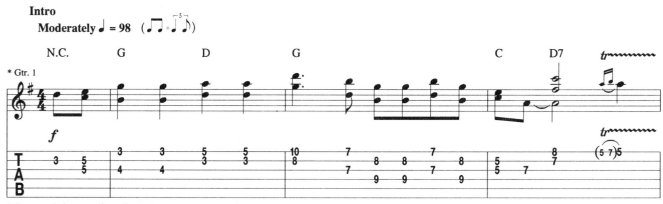

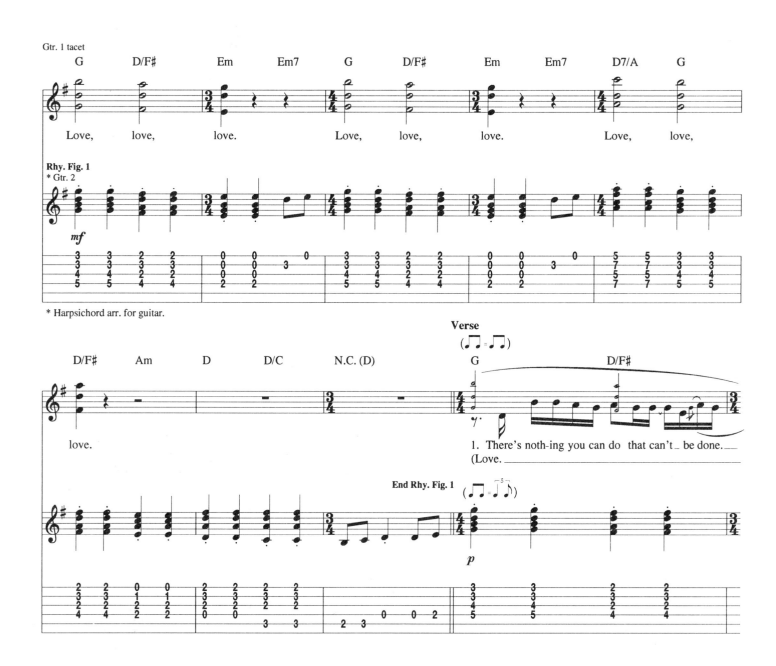

Guitar Solo

Gtr. 2: w/ Rhy. Fig. 1

Chorus

Gtr. 3 tacet

I Am The Walrus

Words and Music By John Lennon And Paul McCartney

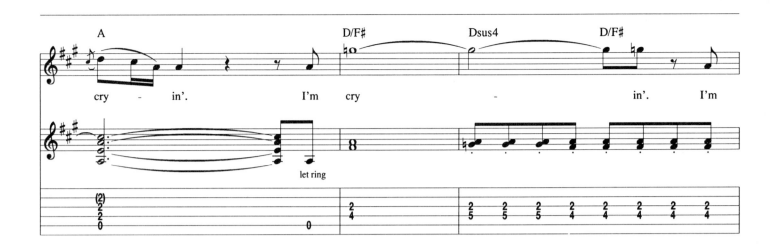

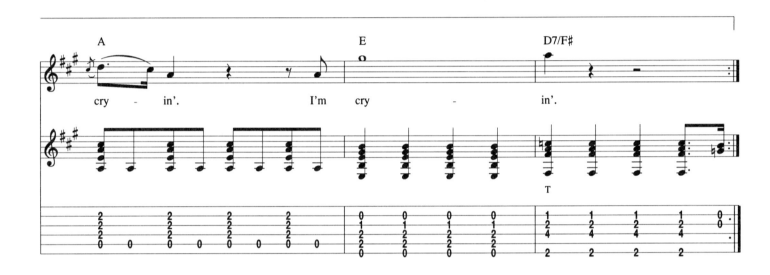

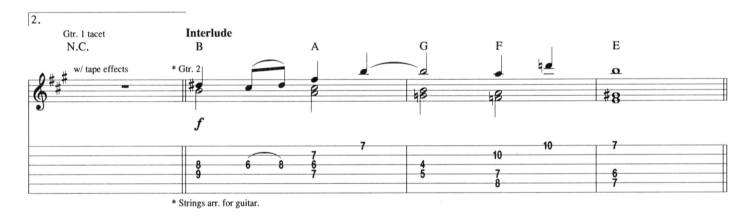

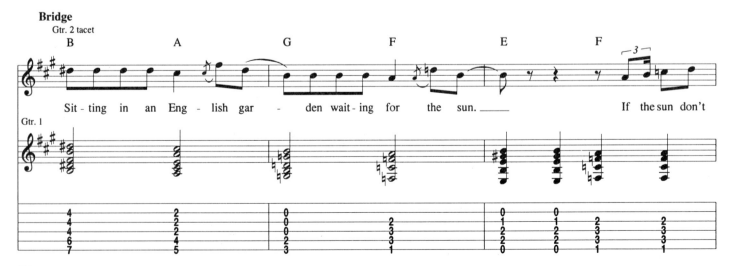

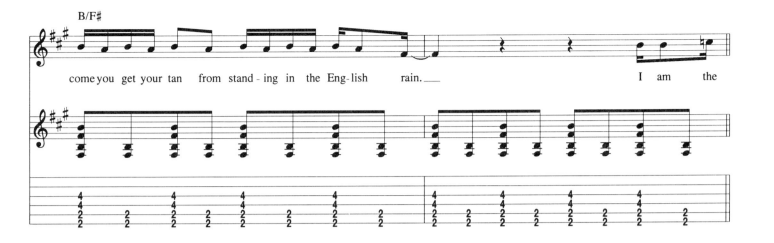

come you get your tan from stand-ing in the Eng-lish rain. ___ I am the

Chorus

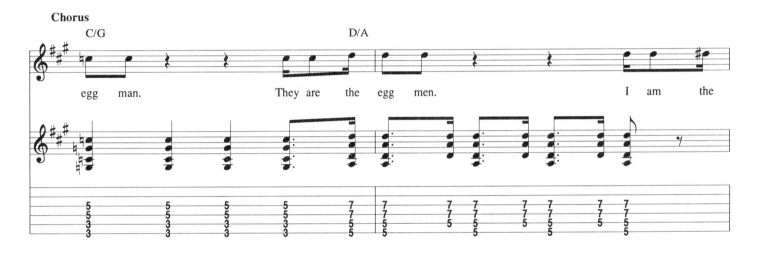

egg man. They are the egg men. I am the

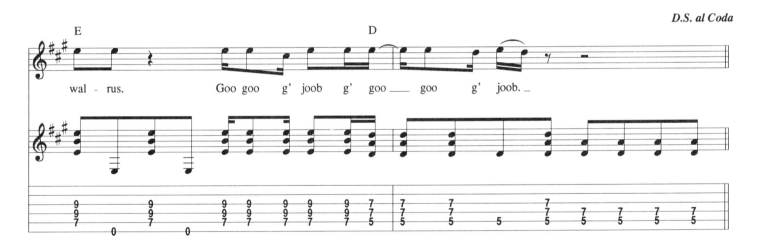

wal - rus. Goo goo g' joob g' goo ___ goo g' joob. ___

D.S. al Coda

⊕ Coda

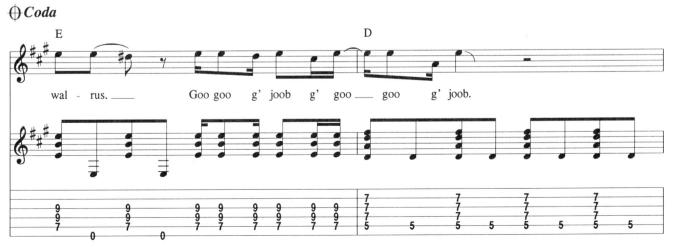

wal - rus. ___ Goo goo g' joob g' goo ___ goo g' joob.

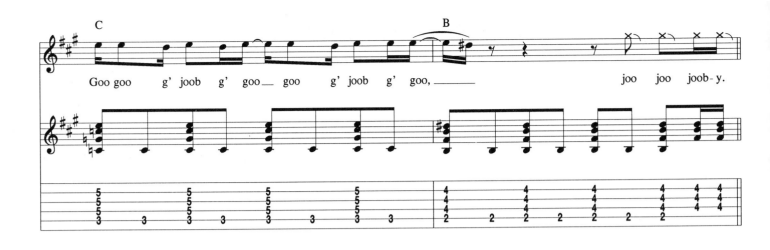

Goo goo g' joob g' goo_ goo g' joob g' goo, _____ joo joo joob-y.

Outro

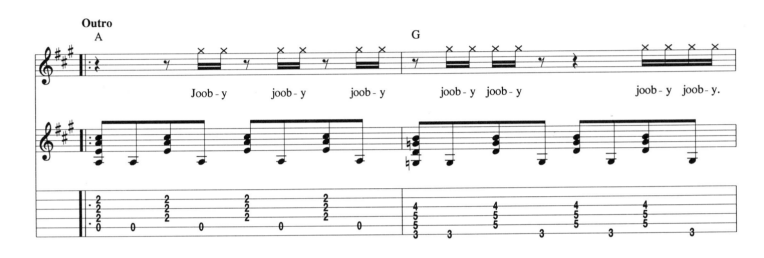

Joob-y joob-y joob-y joob-y joob-y joob-y joob-y.

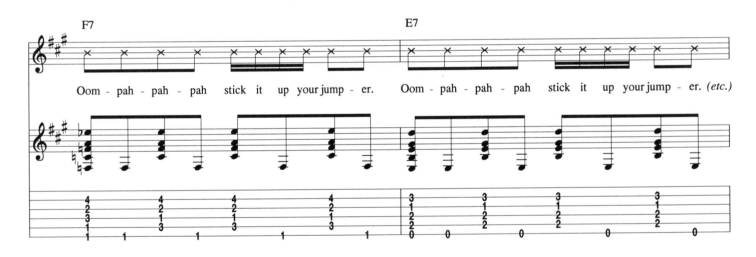

Oom - pah - pah - pah stick it up your jump-er. Oom - pah - pah - pah stick it up your jump-er. *(etc.)*

Play 4 Times And Fade
(w/ad lib vocals and tape effects)

58

Hello, Goodbye

Words and Music by John Lennon and Paul McCartney

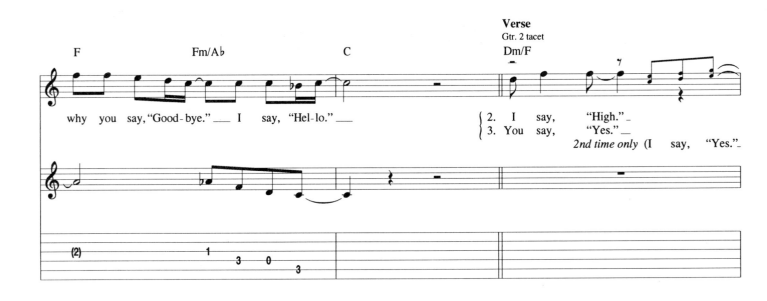

why you say, "Good-bye." ___ I say, "Hel-lo." ___

2. I say, "High." _
3. You say, "Yes." _

2nd time only (I say, "Yes." _

You say, "Low." _ You say, "Why?" _ And I say, "I ___ don't know."
I say, "No." _ You say, "Stop." _ And I say, "Go, ___ go, ___ go."
___ You're tell - ing me, "No." _ I can stay ___ 'till it's time to

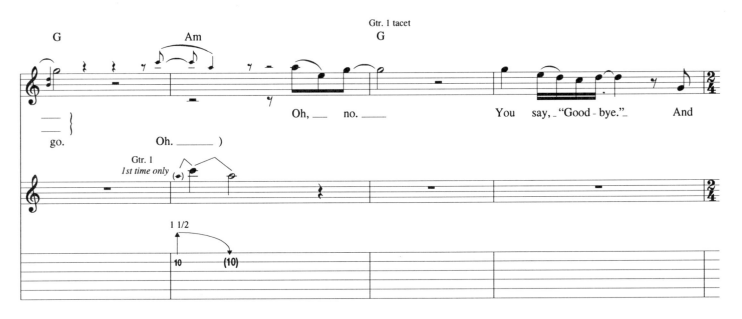

Oh, ___ no. ___ You say, ___ "Good - bye." _ And
go. Oh. _____)

Gtr. 1
1st time only

1 1/2

Chorus

I say, "Hel-lo, _____ hel - lo, ___ hel - lo." ___ I don't ___ know
1st time only (Hel - lo, good - bye, hel - lo, good - bye. _____ Hel - lo, good - bye. _

Gtr. 2

The Fool On The Hill

Words and Music by John Lennon and Paul McCartney

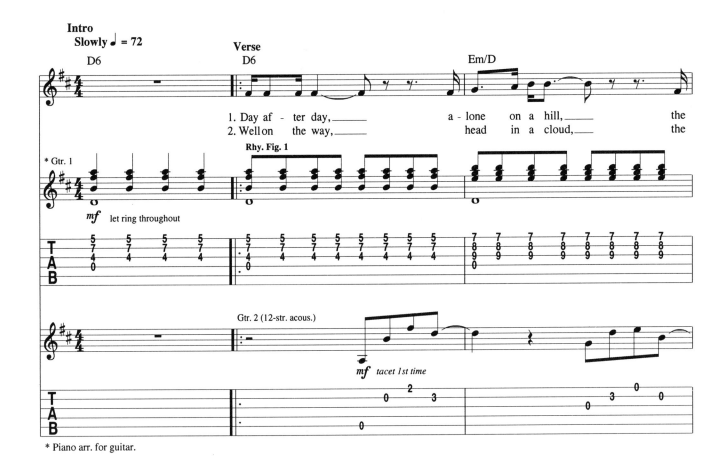

* Piano arr. for guitar.

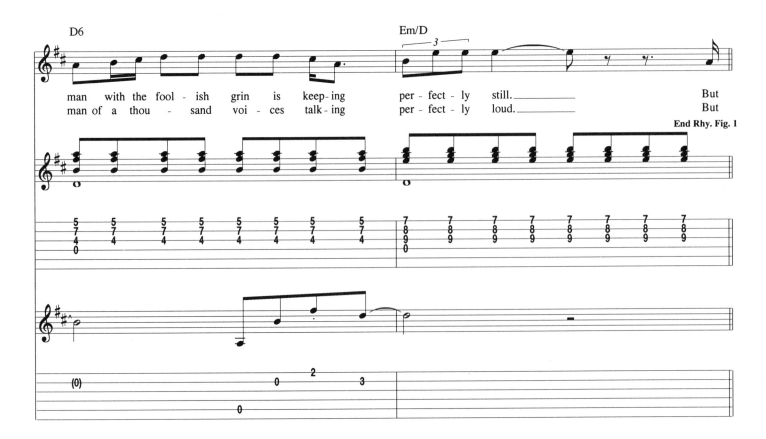

Magical Mystery Tour

Words and Music by John Lennon and Paul McCartney

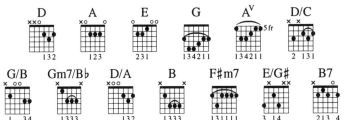

Lady Madonna

Words and Music by John Lennon and Paul McCartney

*Chord symbols implied by piano.

*2nd and 3rd times

Hey Jude

Words and Music by John Lennon and Paul McCartney

Revolution

Words and Music by John Lennon and Paul McCartney

† All Gtrs: Capo II

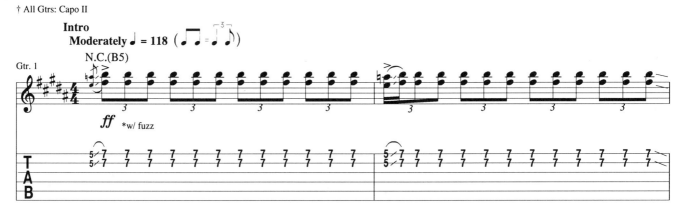

*Fuzztone results from overloading the mixing console input.

†Notes tabbed at 2nd fret played as open strings.

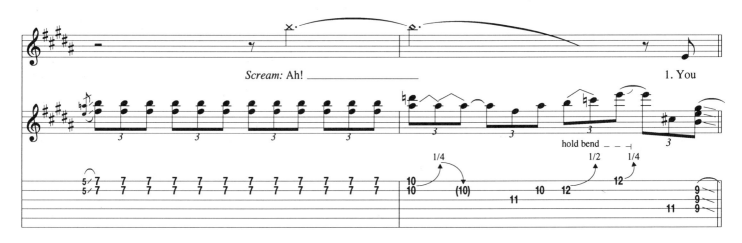

*Tie 1st time only.

we all want _ to change the world.
we'd all love _ to see the plan.
we all want _ to change your head.

You
You
You

tell me that it's ev-o-lu-tion,_____ well,_____ you know,___
ask me for a con-tri-bu-tion,_____ well,_____ you know,___
tell me it's the in-sti-tu-tion,_____ well,_____ you know,___

we all want ___ to change the world. _____
we are do - in' what we can. _____
you bet - ter free your mind in - stead. _____

Pre - Chorus

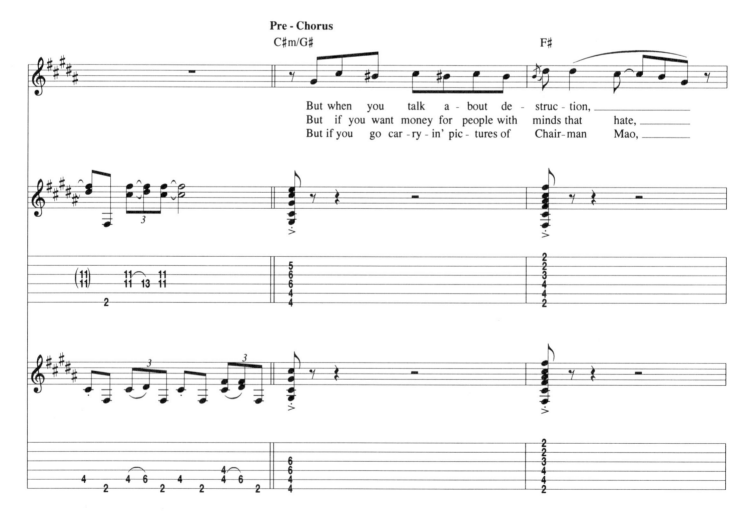

But when you talk a - bout de - struc - tion, _____
But if you want money for people with minds that hate, _____
But if you go car - ry - in' pic - tures of Chair - man Mao, _____

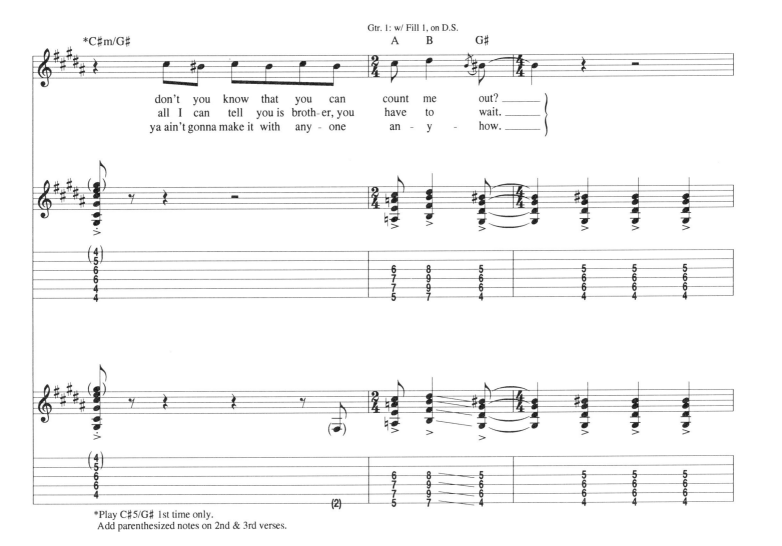

don't you know that you can count me out? ____
all I can tell you is broth-er, you have to wait. ____
ya ain't gonna make it with any-one an - y - how.

*Play C#5/G# 1st time only.
Add parenthesized notes on 2nd & 3rd verses.

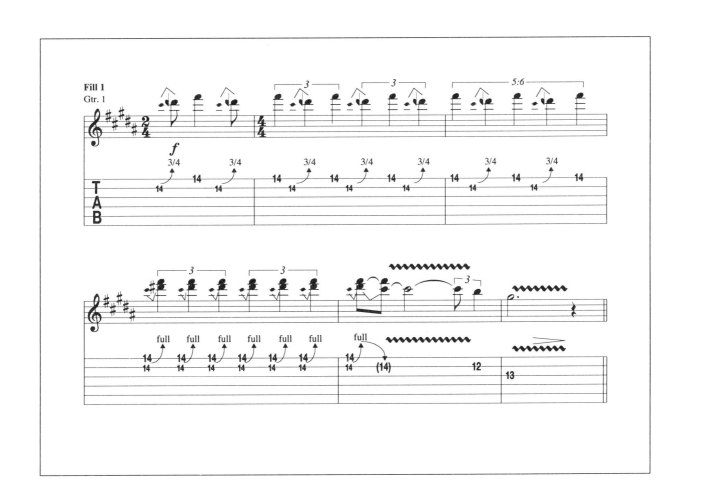

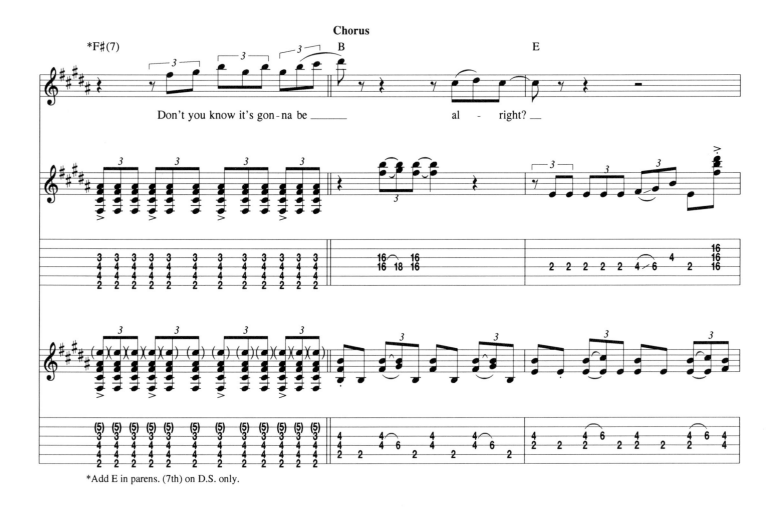

*Add E in parens. (7th) on D.S. only.

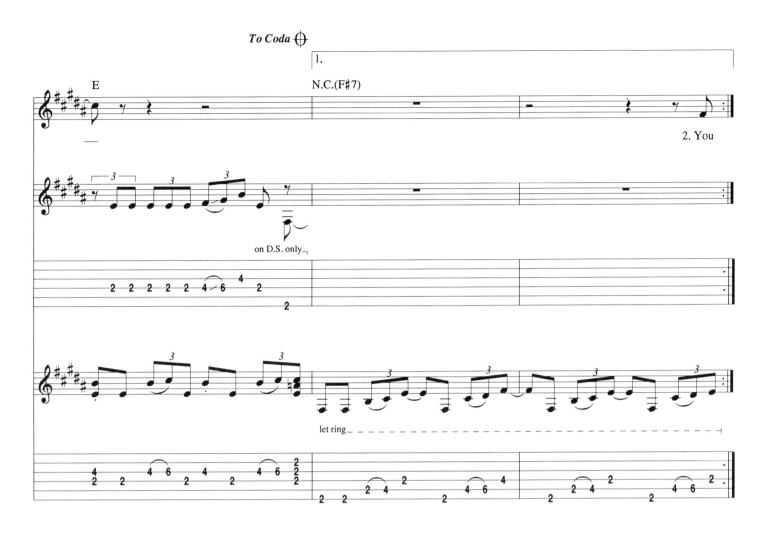

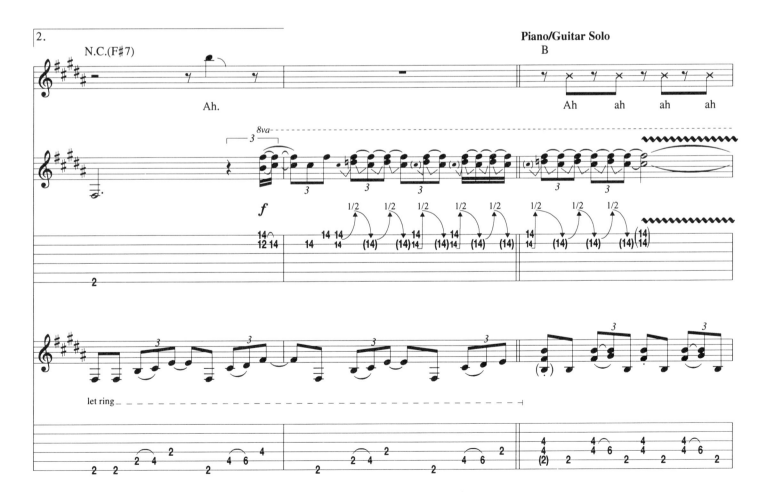

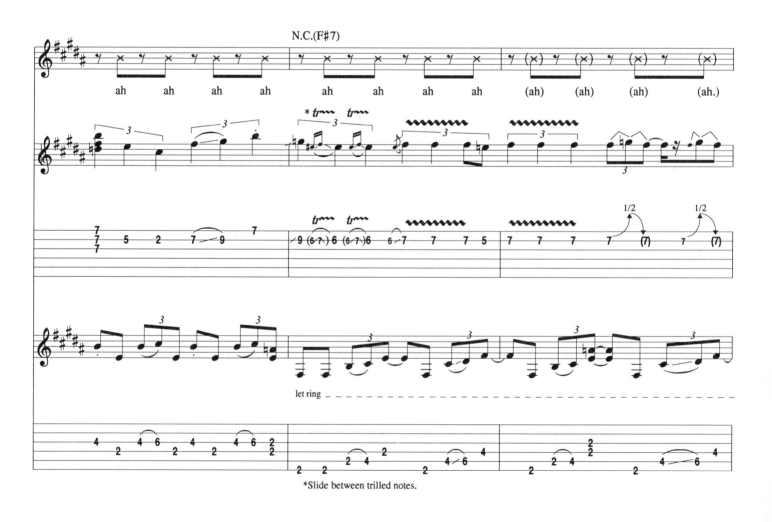

*Slide between trilled notes.

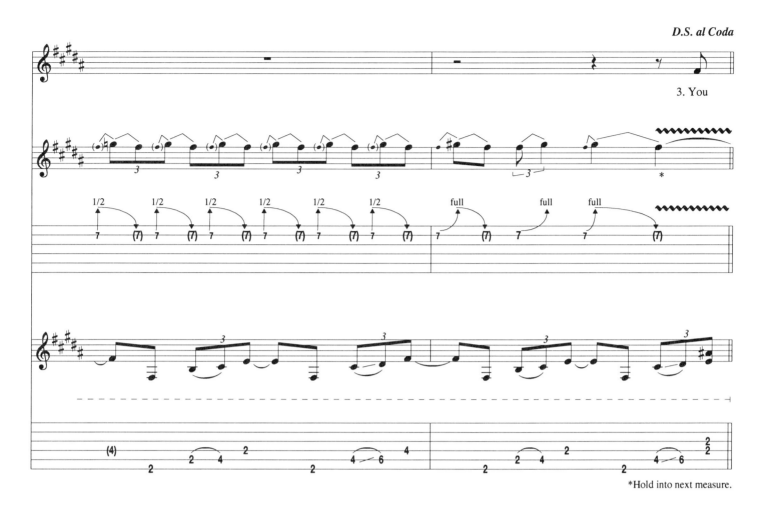

3. You

*Hold into next measure.

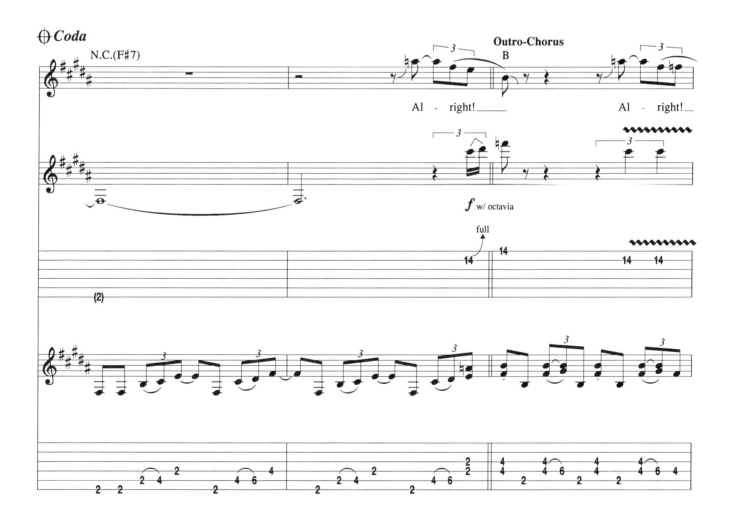

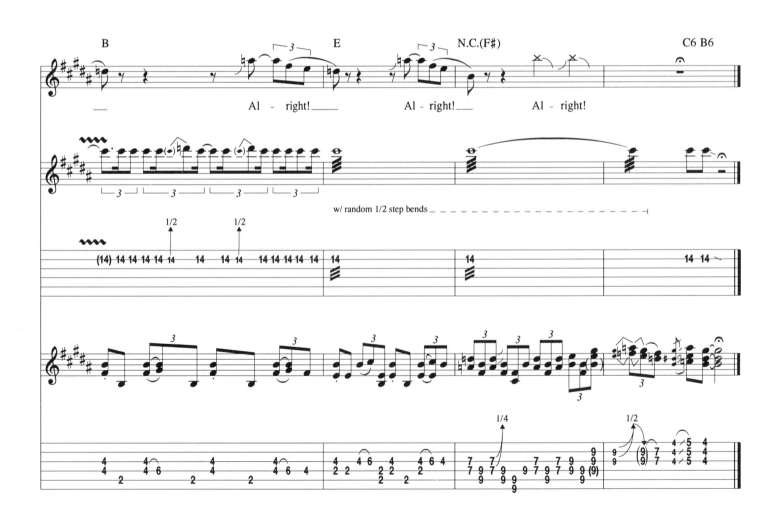

Back In The U.S.S.R.

Words and Music by John Lennon and Paul McCartney

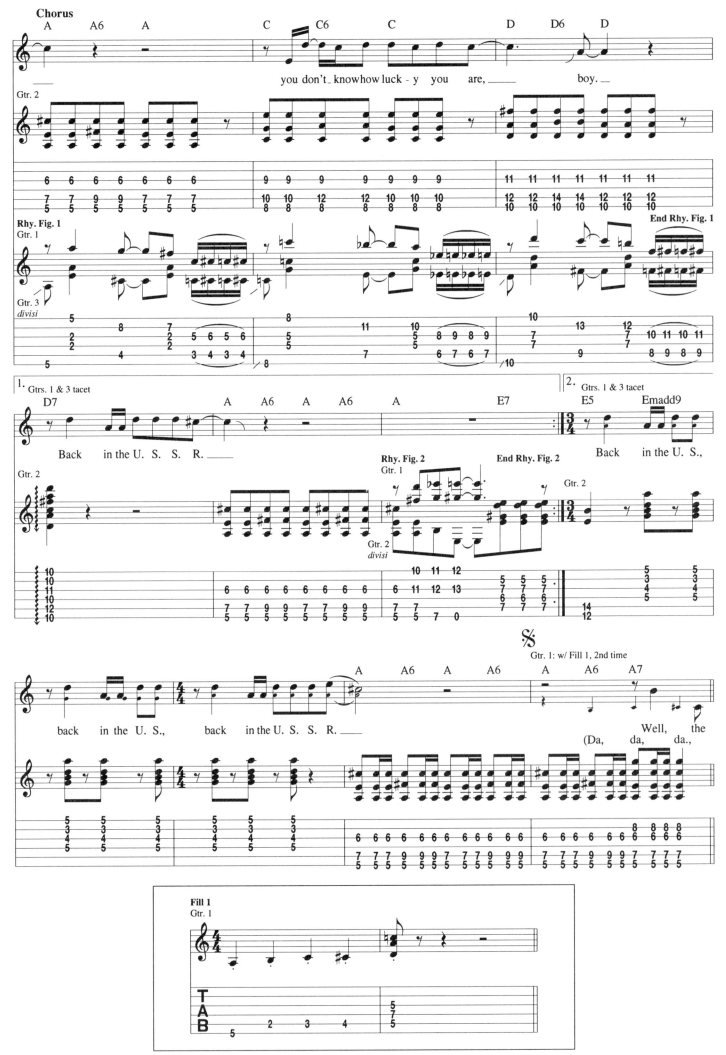

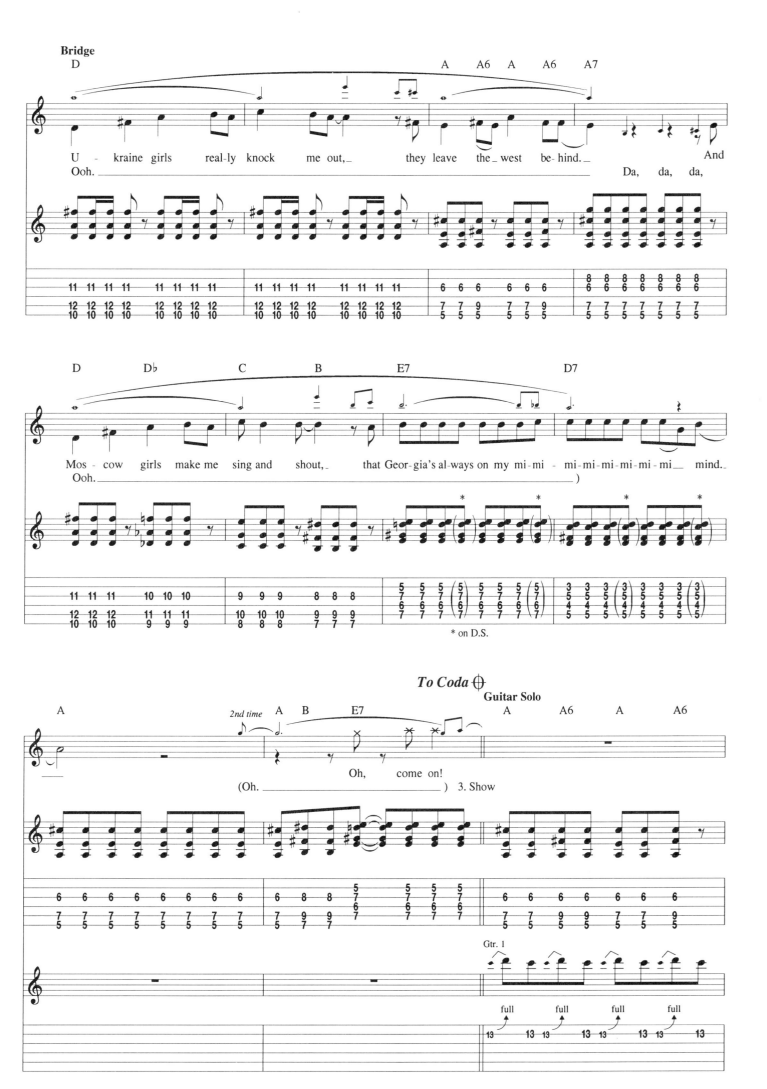

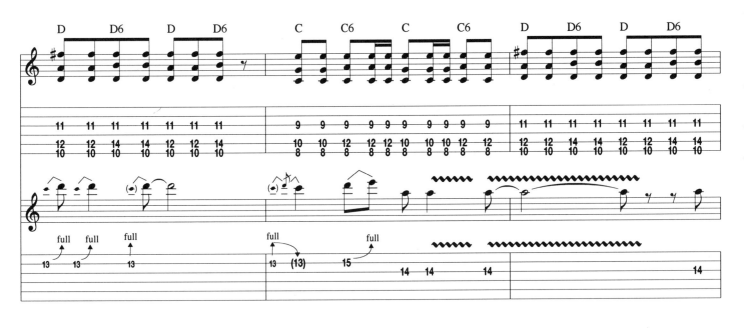

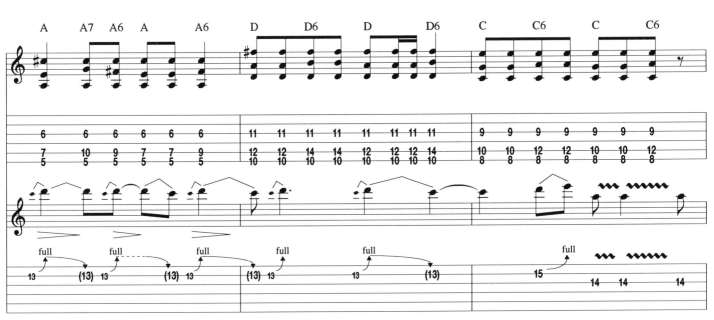

Chorus

Gtrs. 1 & 3: w/ Rhy. Fig. 1

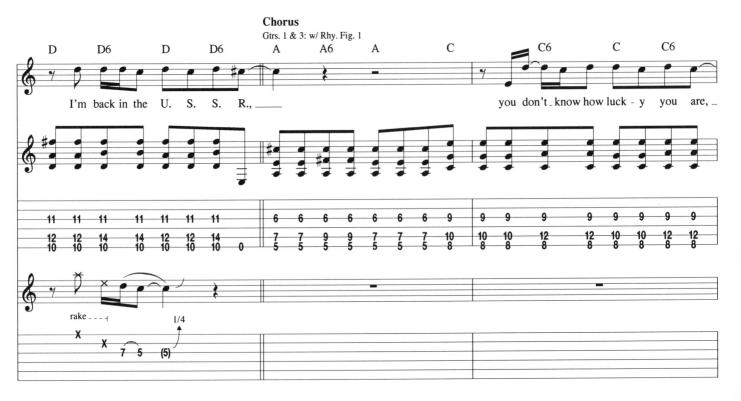

I'm back in the U. S. S. R., _____ you don't know how luck-y you are, _____

While My Guitar Gently Weeps

By George Harrison

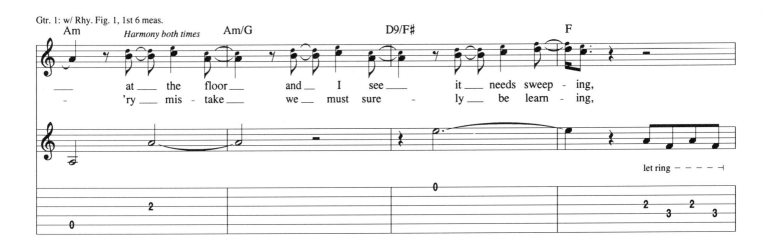

Gtr. 1: w/ Rhy. Fig. 1, 1st 6 meas.

Harmony both times

at ___ the floor ___ and I see ___ it ___ needs sweep - ing,
'ry ___ mis - take ___ we ___ must sure - ly be learn - ing,

let ring - - - - -

Gtr. 2: w/ Fill 3, 2nd time

To Coda 1

Gtr. 1

still my gui - tar ___ gent - ly weeps. ___

full

full

full

Bridge

Gtr. 2: w/ Fill 4, 2nd time

Rhy. Fig. 2

I don't know why _____
I don't know how _____ you ___ were di - ver - ted,

no - bod - y told ___ you

let ring - - - - - - - -

*

1/2

*2nd time, simile

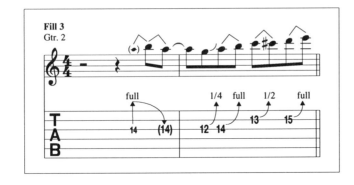

Fill 3
Gtr. 2

full   1/4 full 1/2 full

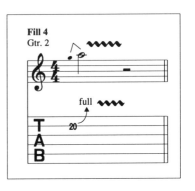

Fill 4
Gtr. 2

full

how_ to un-fold _____ your_ love.
you_ were per-ver _____ -ted, _____ too.

Gtr. 1: w/ Rhy. Fig. 2, simile

I don't know how_____
I don't know how_____
some - one con-trolled you,
you_ were in - ver - ted,

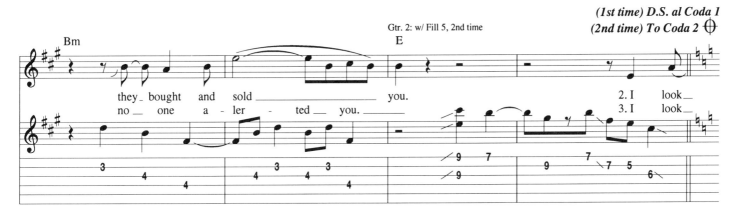

(1st time) D.S. al Coda 1
(2nd time) To Coda 2 ⊕

Gtr. 2: w/ Fill 5, 2nd time

they_ bought and sold _____ you.
no_ one a - ler - ted_ you. _____
2. I look_
3. I look_

⊕ *Coda 1*

Guitar Solo

Gtr. 1: w/ Rhy. Fig. 1, 1st 7 meas.

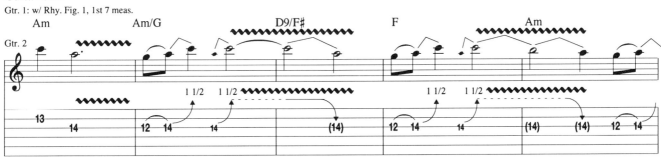

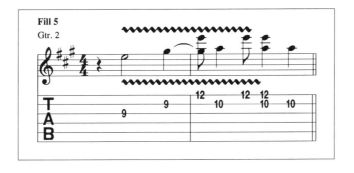

Ob - La - Di, Ob - La - Da

Words and Music by John Lennon and Paul McCartney

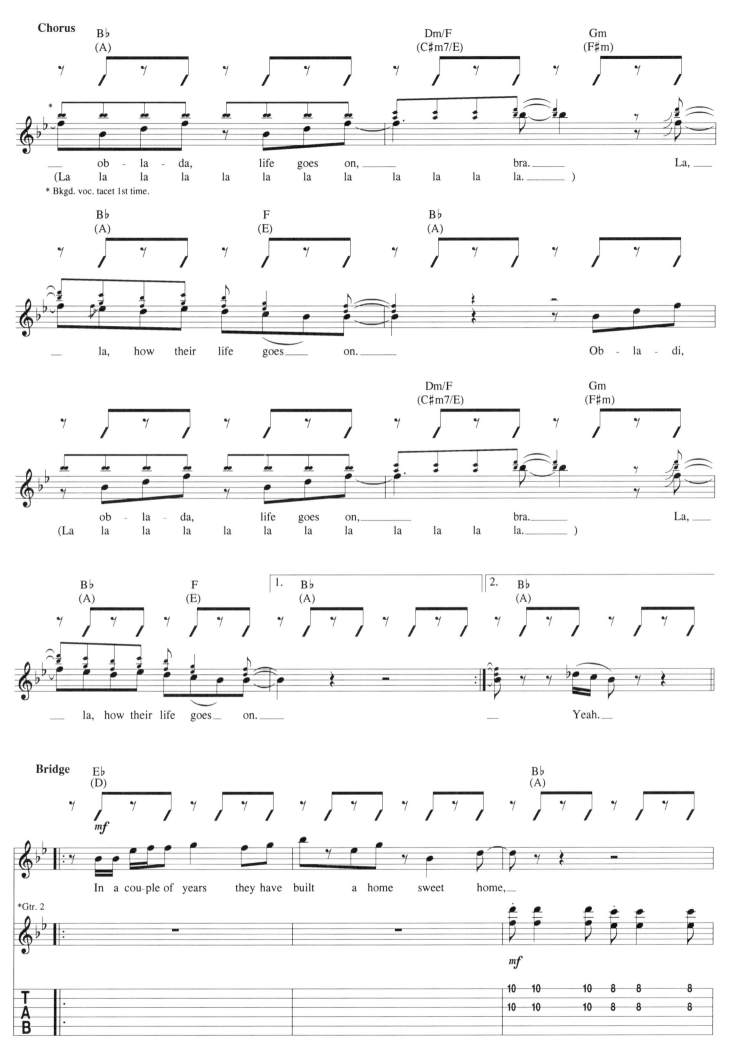

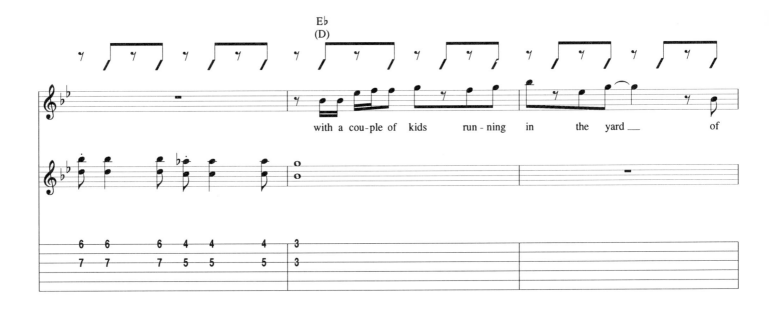

with a cou-ple of kids run-ning in the yard ___ of

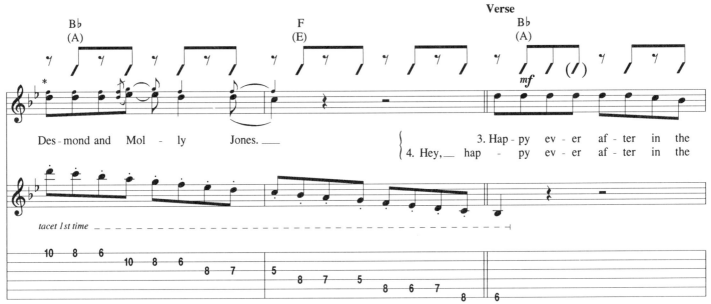

Des-mond and Mol - ly Jones. ___

3. Hap - py ev - er af - ter in the
4. Hey, ___ hap - py ev - er af - ter in the

tacet 1st time

* Bkgd. voc. tacet 1st time.

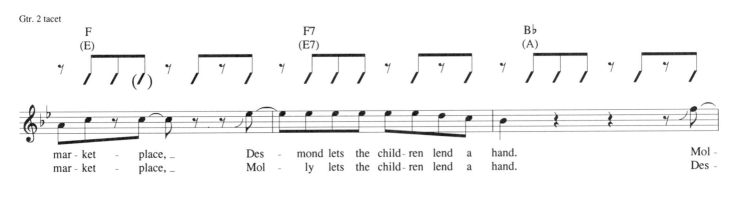

Gtr. 2 tacet

mar - ket - place, ___ Des - mond lets the child - ren lend a hand. Mol -
mar - ket - place, ___ Mol - ly lets the child - ren lend a hand. Des -

- ly stays at home and does her pret - ty face ___ and in the eve - ning she still sings it with the band. ___
- mond stays at home and does his pret - ty face ___ and in the eve - ning she's a sing - er with the band. ___

Chorus

Yes, —
Yeah, — } ob-la-di, ob-la-da, life goes on, — bra.— La, — la, how their life goes on.—

Gtr. 2

* Bkgd. voc. tacet 1st time.

Hey, — ob-la-di, ob-la-da, life goes on, — bra.— La, — la, how their life goes — on.—

* Bkgd. voc. tacet 1st time.

Outro
Gtr. 2 tacet

Well, if you want some fun,— take ob-la-di-bla-da. (Thank you.)

Get Back

Words and Music by John Lennon and Paul McCartney

Intro
Moderate Rock ♩ = 123

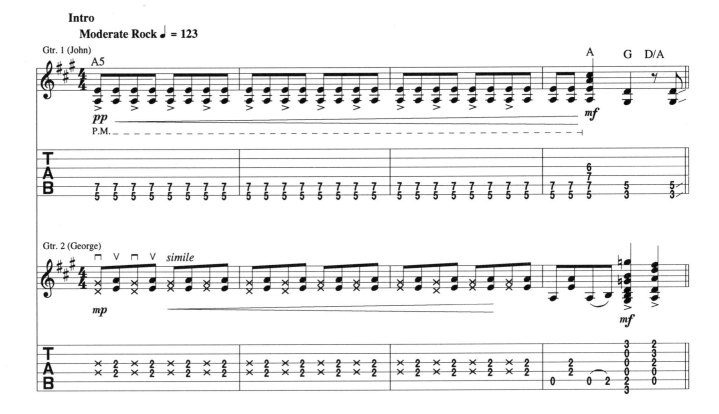

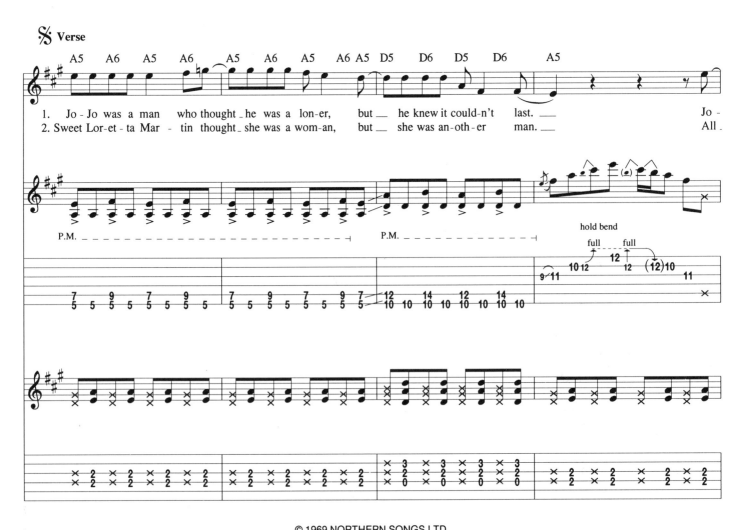

Chord symbols reflect overall harmony.

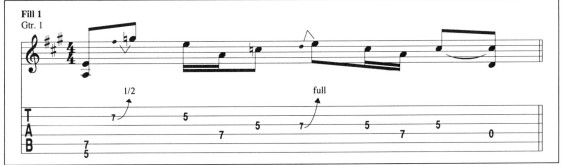

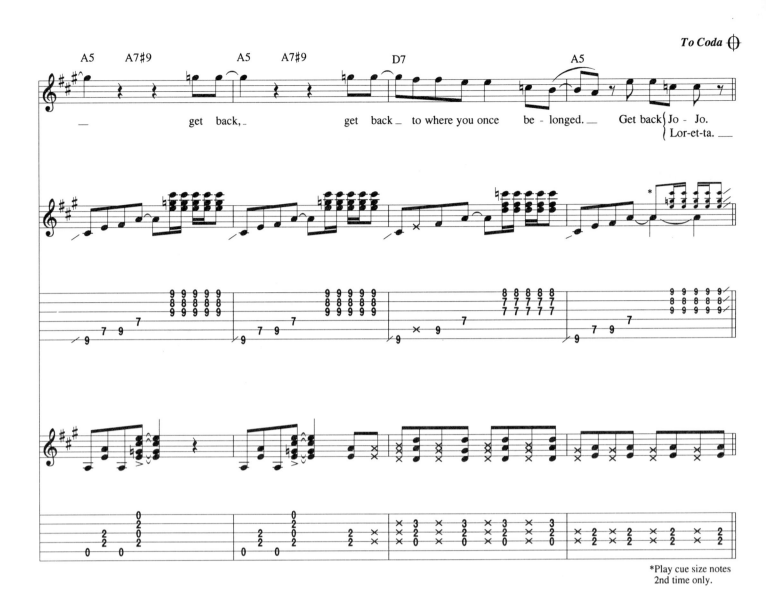

*Play cue size notes
2nd time only.

Guitar Solo

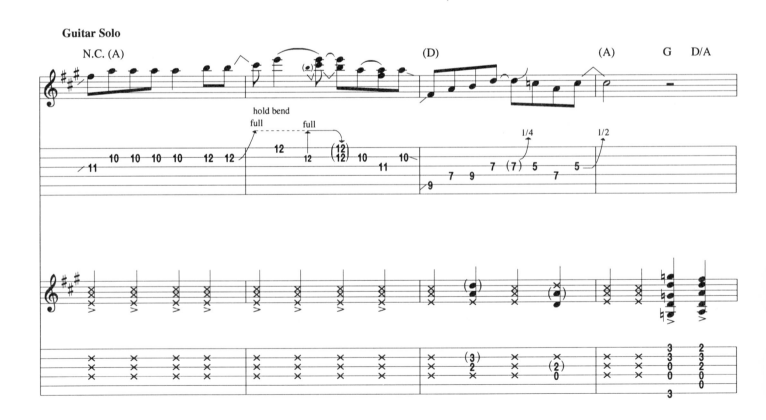

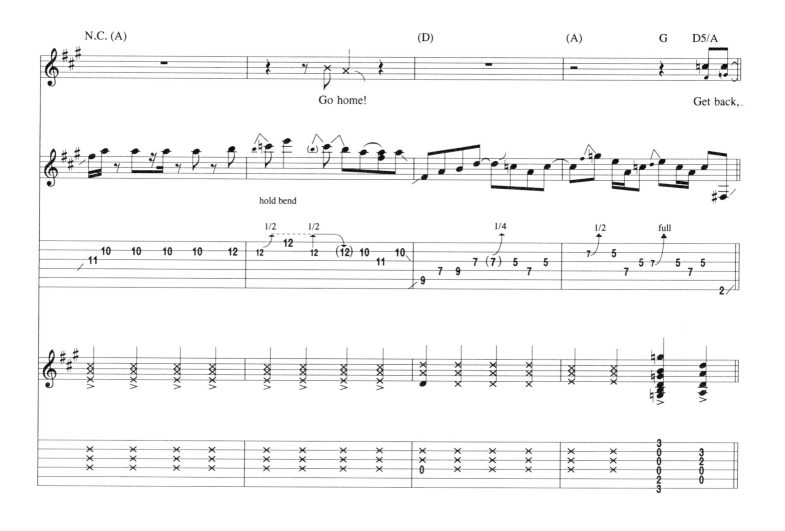

Chorus

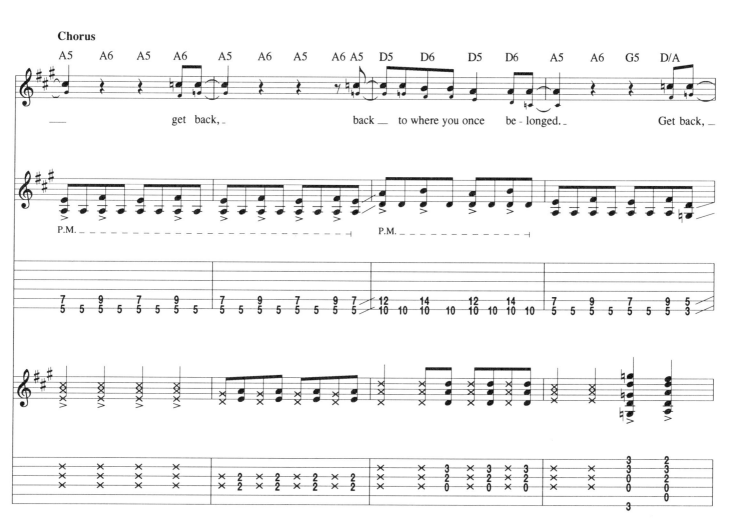

get back, —   back — to where you once   be - longed. —   Here.

*Gtr. 3

Gtr. 1

Gtr. 2

*Elec. piano arr. for gtr.

Piano Solo

Uh,   get   back   Jo!

⊕ *Coda*

Guitar Solo

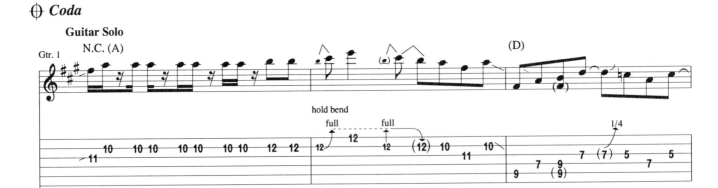

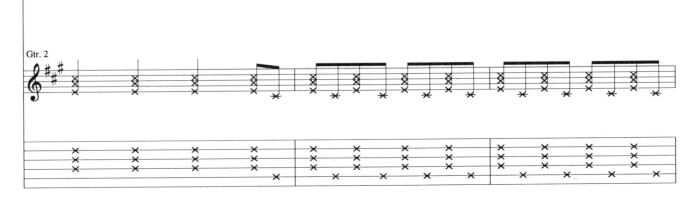

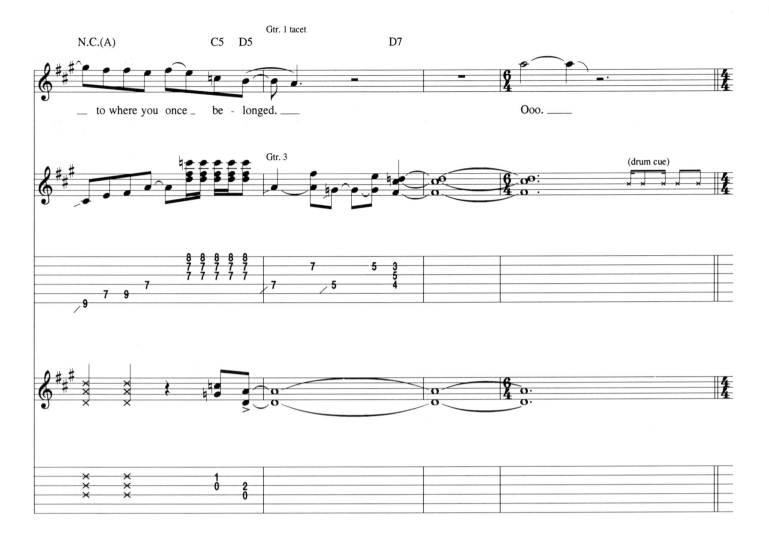

to where you once be - longed. _____ Ooo. _____

Outro

Gtr. 3 tacet

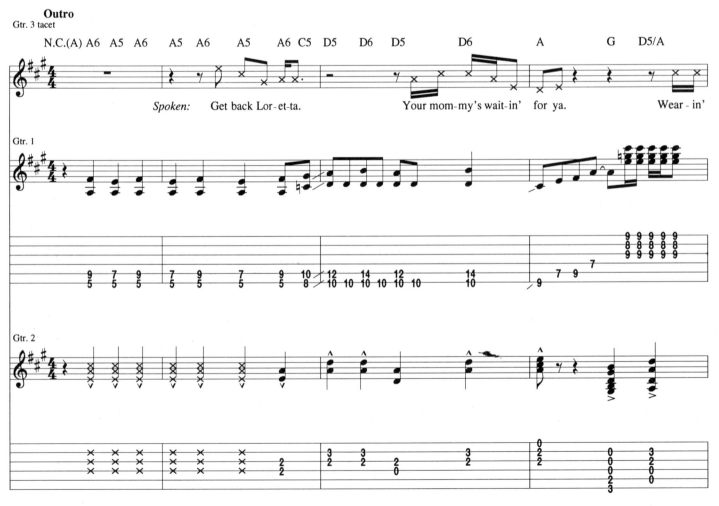

Spoken: Get back Lor-et-ta.

Your mom-my's wait-in' for ya.

Wear - in'

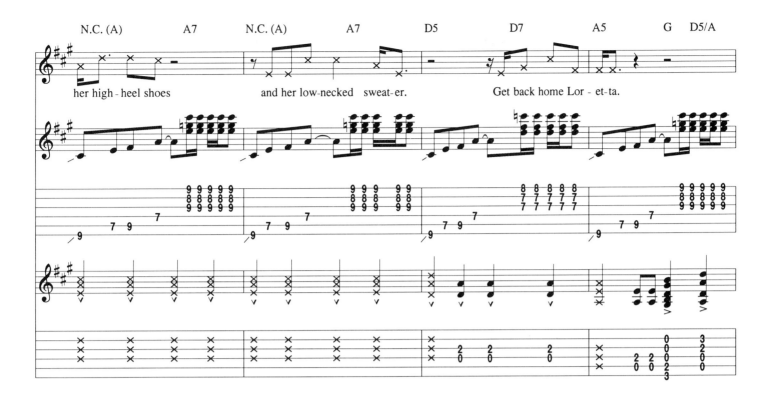

her high-heel shoes   and her low-necked sweat-er.   Get back home Lor - et-ta.

Lead voc. ad lib till fade

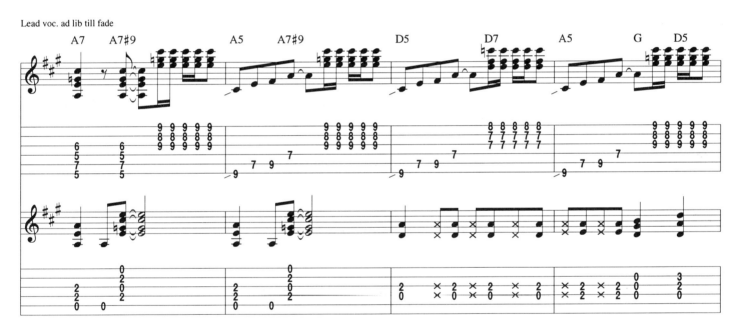

Begin Fade   ***Fade Out***

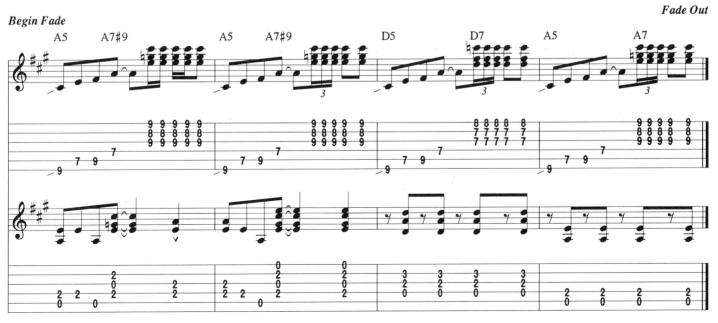

Don't Let Me Down

Words and Music by John Lennon and Paul McCartney

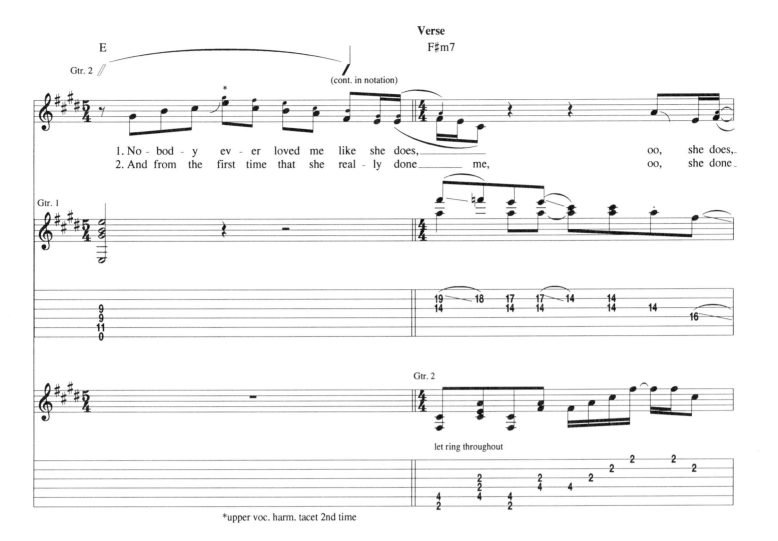

1. No-bod-y ev-er loved me like she does,_____ oo, she does,

2. And from the first time that she real-ly done_____ me, oo, she done_

*upper voc. harm. tacet 2nd time

_____ me, she done _ me good. _____

yes, _ she does. _

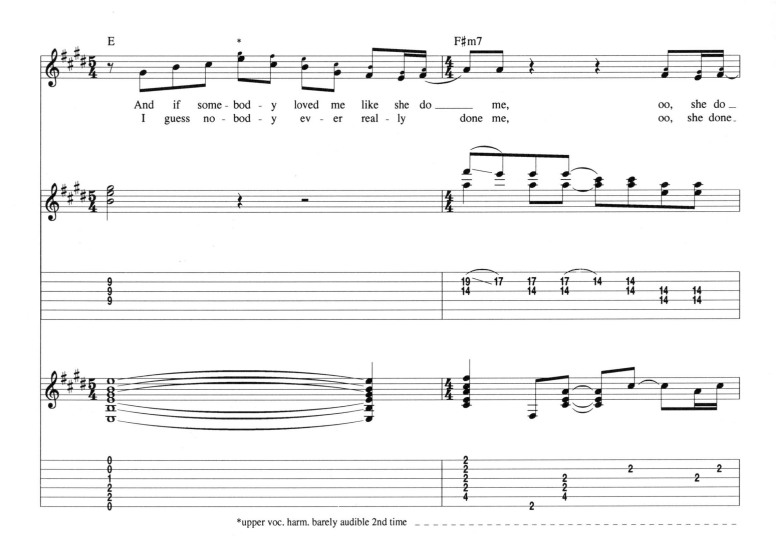

*upper voc. harm. barely audible 2nd time

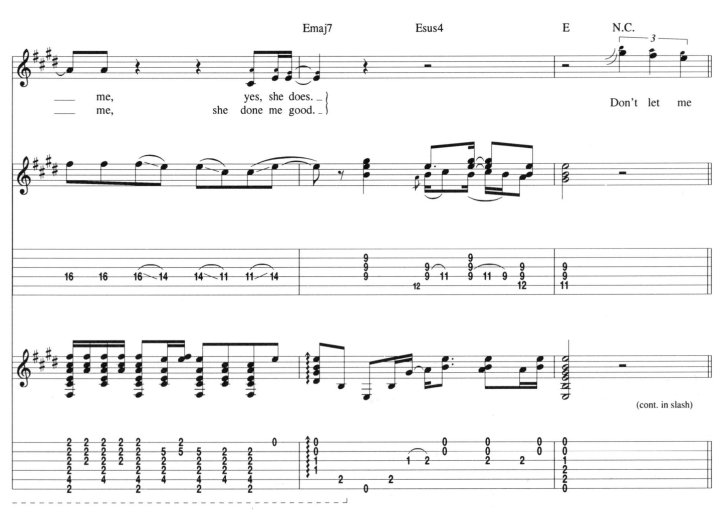

(cont. in slash)

The Ballad Of John And Yoko

Words and Music by John Lennon and Paul McCartney

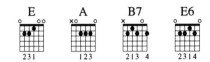

1. Stand - in' in the dock at South Hamp -
2. Fin - 'ly made the plane in - to Par -
   Par - is to the Am - ster - dam Hil -

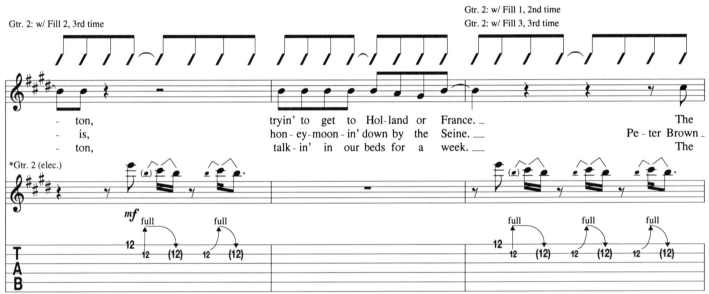

- ton,
- is,
- ton,

tryin' to get to Hol - land or France. _
hon - ey - moon - in' down by the Seine. _
talk - in' in our beds for a week. _

The
The Pe - ter Brown _
The

*Two gtrs. arr. for one.

Fill 1

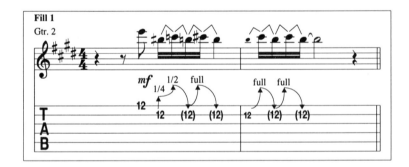

Fill 2

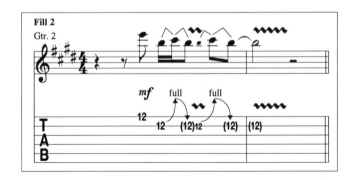

Fill 3

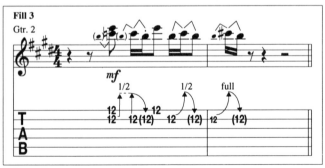

man in the mac __ said, "You've got - ta go back." You know they did - n't e - ven give us a chance.
__ called to say, __ "You can make it O. K., you can get mar - ried in Gib - ral - tar near Spain."
news - peo - ple said, __ "Say, what - cha do - in' in bed?" I said, "We're on - ly tryin' to get us some peace."

Chorus
A

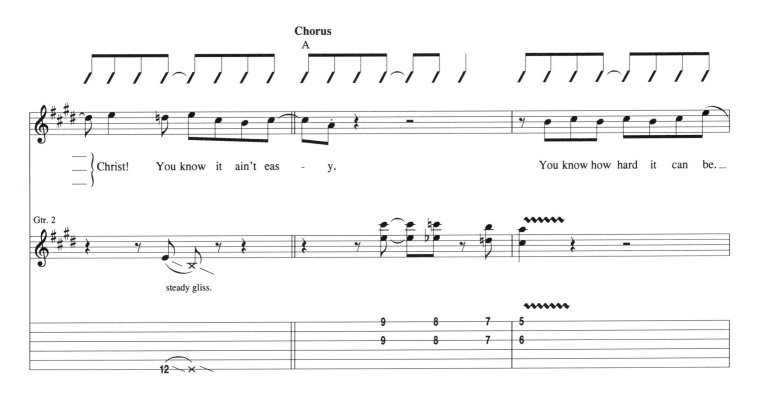

__ Christ! You know it ain't eas - y. You know how hard it can be. __

Gtr. 2

steady gliss.

E   B7

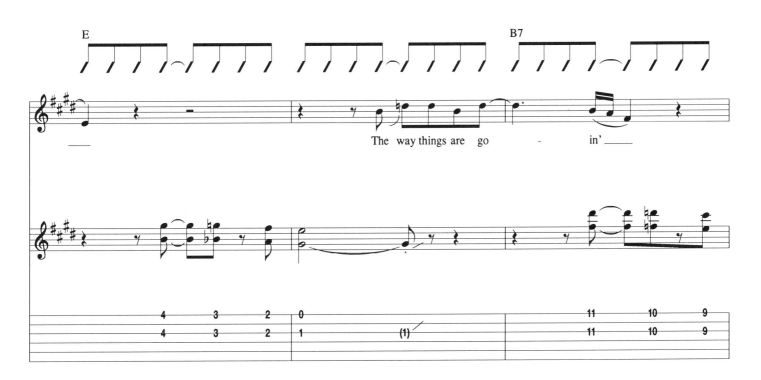

The way things are go - in' __

they're gon - na cru - ci - fy ____ me.

3. Drove from

Sav - in' up your mon - ey for a

steady gliss. P.M. throughout

rain - y day, ____ giv - in' all your clothes to char - i - ty.

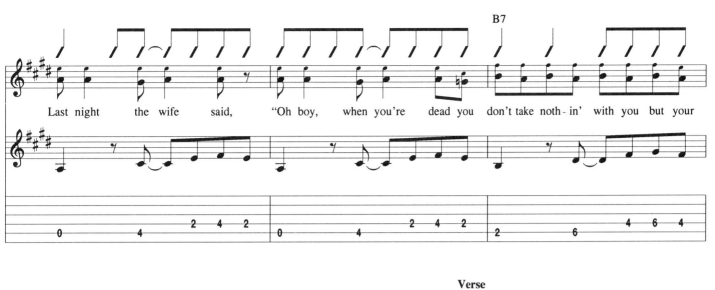

Last night the wife said, "Oh boy, when you're dead you don't take noth-in' with you but your

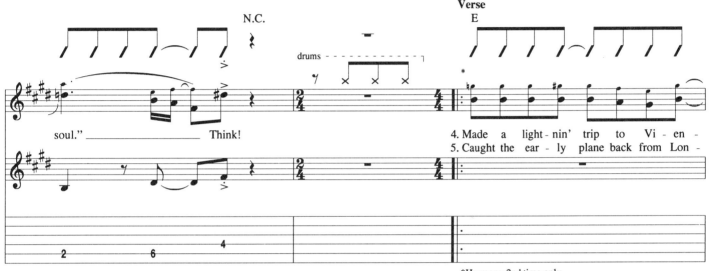

soul." _____ Think!

4. Made a light-nin' trip to Vi-en-
5. Caught the ear-ly plane back from Lon-

*Harmony 2nd time only.

Gtr. 2: w/ Fill 4, 2nd time   Gtr. 2: w/ Fill 5, 2nd time

- na,
- don,   eat-ing choc'-late cake in a bag. _____   The
                          fif-ty a-corns tied in a sack. _____   The

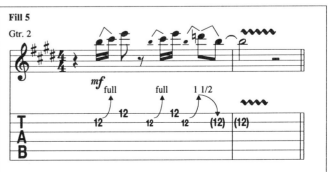

news-pa-per said, ____ "She's gone to his head. ____ They look just like two Gu-rus in drag."
men from the press ____ said, "We wish you suc-cess. ____ It's good to have the both of you back."

Chorus

____ Christ! You know it ain't eas - y. You know how hard it can be. ____

steady gliss.

The way things are go - in' ____

* Gtr. 2 indicated to right of slash.

Old Brown Shoe

Words and Music by George Harrison

* piano and bass arr. for gtr.

*Chord symbols reflect overall harmony.

Verse

1. I want a love that's right, right is on-ly half of what's wrong.
pick me up from where some try to drag me down.
love is yours to miss, that love is some-thin' I'd hate.

I want a short - haired girl who
And when I see your smile re - plac
I'll make an ear - ly start, I'm mak -

some - times wears it twice as long.
- ing ev - 'ry thought - less frown.
- ing sure that I'm not late.

Now,

Here Comes The Sun

Words and Music by George Harrison

*Capo VII

Intro
Moderately ♩ = 126

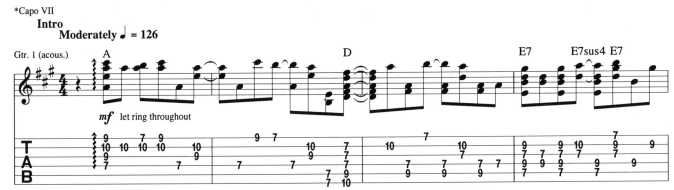

*All notes tabbed on 7th fret are played as open strings

Chorus

Here comes the sun, doo 'n' doo doo. Here comes the sun

'n' I say it's al - right.

Lit - tle dar-lin', it ___ seems ___ like ___ years ___ since it's ___ been ___ clear. ___

Here comes ___ the sun. ___ (Doo 'n' doo doo.) Here comes ___ the sun. ___

It's al - right. It's al - right.

Come Together

Words and Music by John Lennon and Paul McCartney

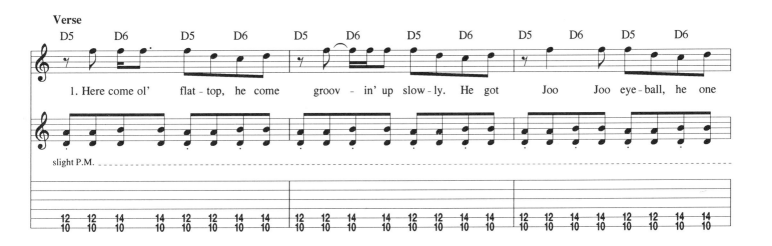

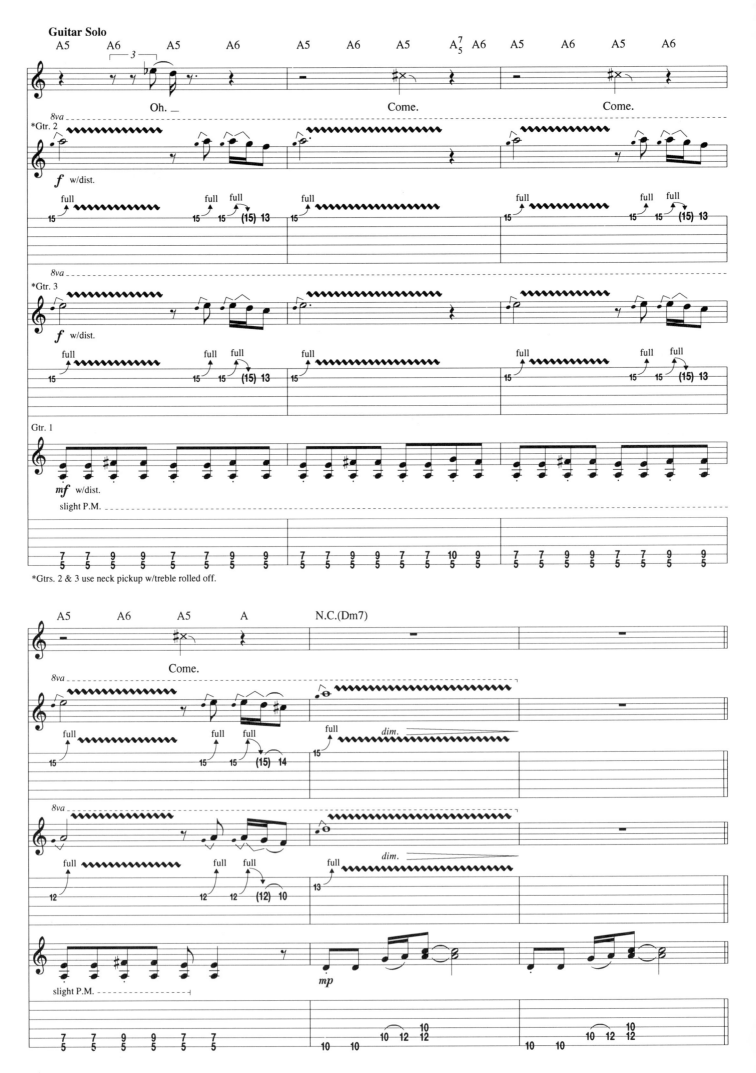

Guitar Solo

*Gtrs. 2 & 3 use neck pickup w/treble rolled off.

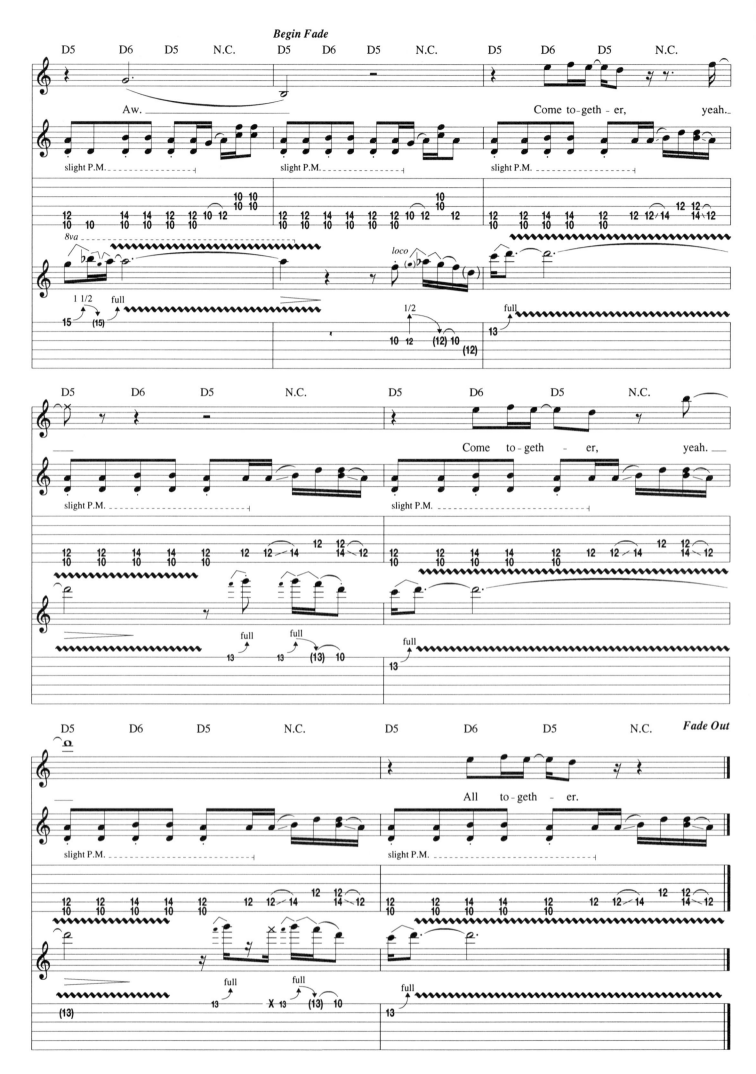

Something

Words and Music by George Harrison

Gtr. 3; "Drop D" Tuning:
①= E ④= D
②= B ⑤= A
③= G ⑥= D
Gtrs. 1 & 2: Standard Tuning

Intro

Slowly ♩ = 66

1. Some - thing in ___ the way   she moves ___
2. Some - where in ___ her smile   she knows ___

at - tracts ___ me like   no   oth - er   lov -
that I ___ don't need   no   oth - er   lov -

- er.
- er.

Some - thing in ___ the way   she ___ woos ___
Some - thing in ___ the style   that ___ shows ___

I don't want to leave_ her now,   you know I be-lieve_ and how. _

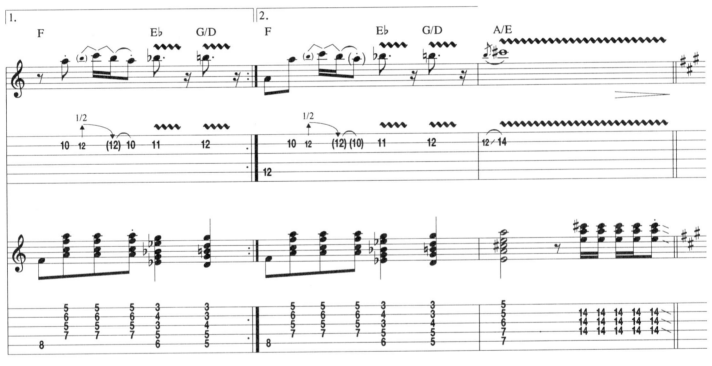

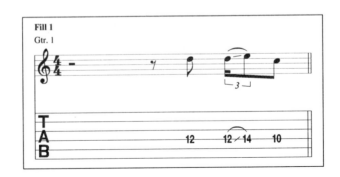

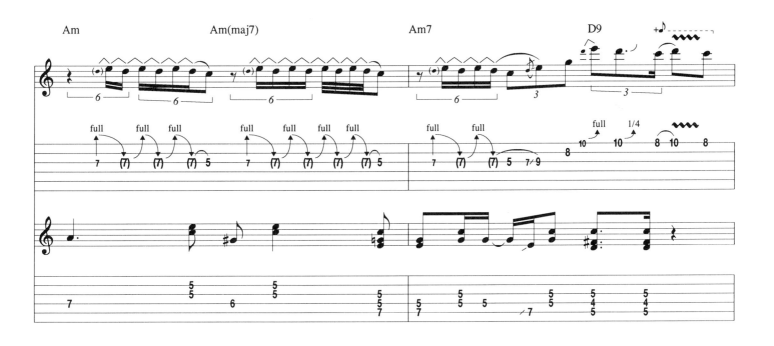

Verse

Gtr. 1 tacet

3. Some-thing in __ the way she knows, __

and all __ I have _____ to do ___ is think of her.

Gtr. 2

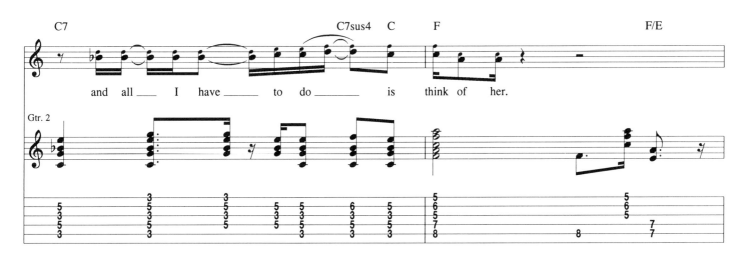

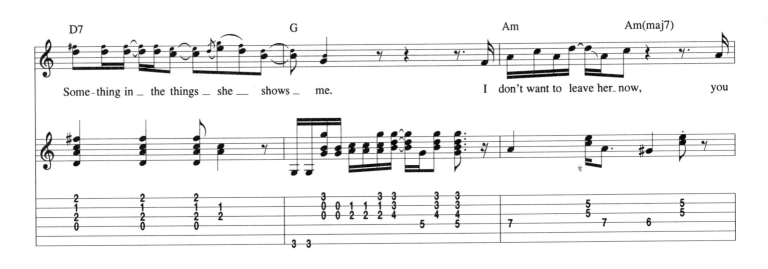

Some-thing in _ the things _ she _ shows _ me. I don't want to leave her _ now, you

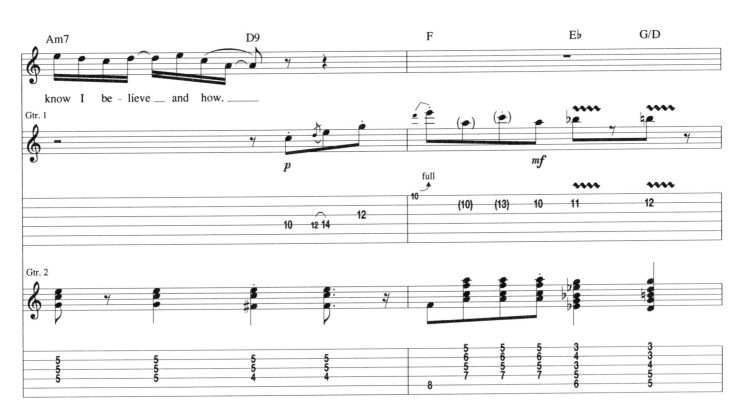

know I be - lieve _ and how. _____

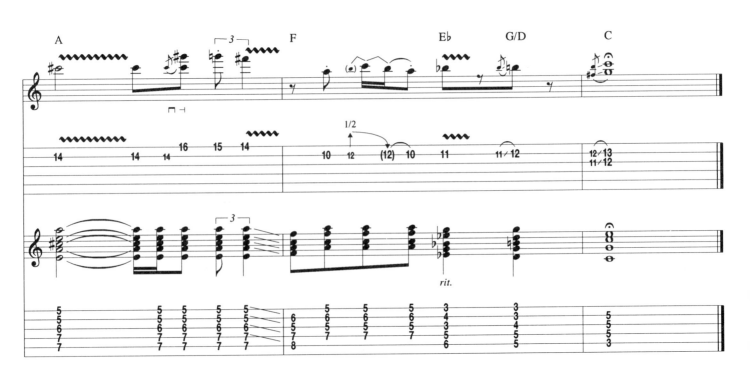

Octopus's Garden

Words and Music by Richard Starkey

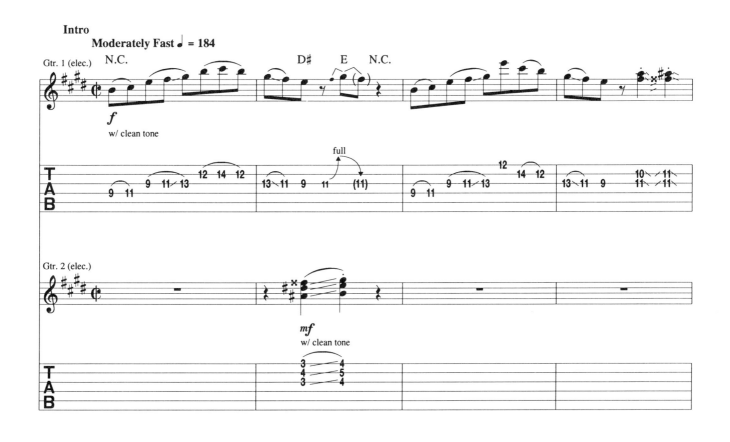

Verse

Gtr. 1 tacet
Gtr. 3: w/ Fill 2, 2nd time

Bkgd. Voc. 2nd time only

1. I'd like to be under the sea
2. We would be warm below the storm
(Ooh.)

in an oc - to - pus's gar - den in the shade.
in our lit - tle hide - a - way be - neath the waves.
(Ooh.)

He'd let us in,
Rest - ing our head
(Ah.)

Fill 2
Gtr. 3

146

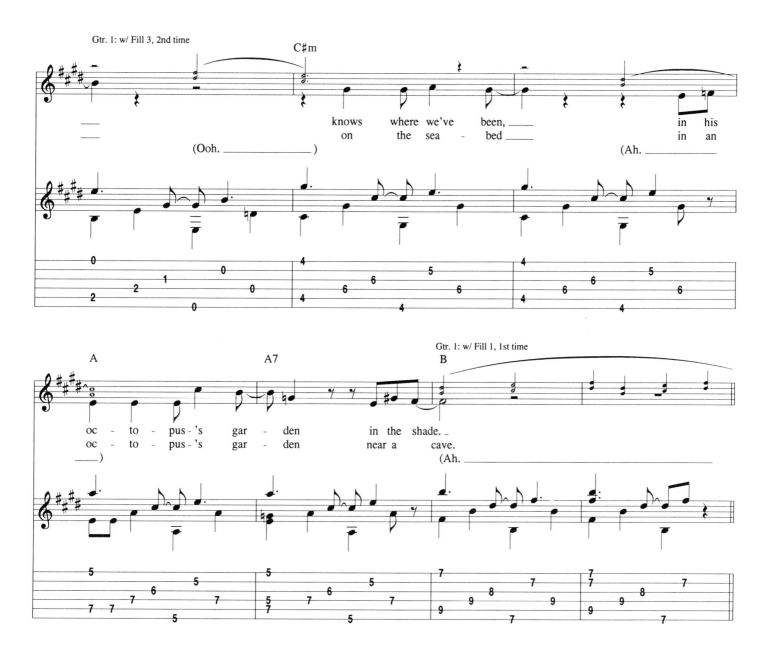

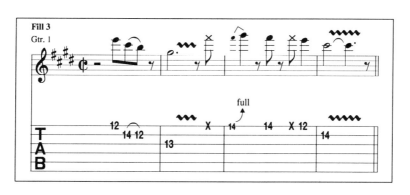

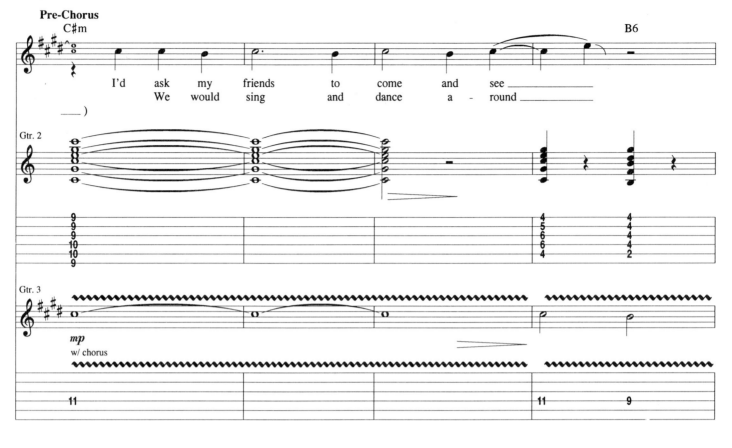

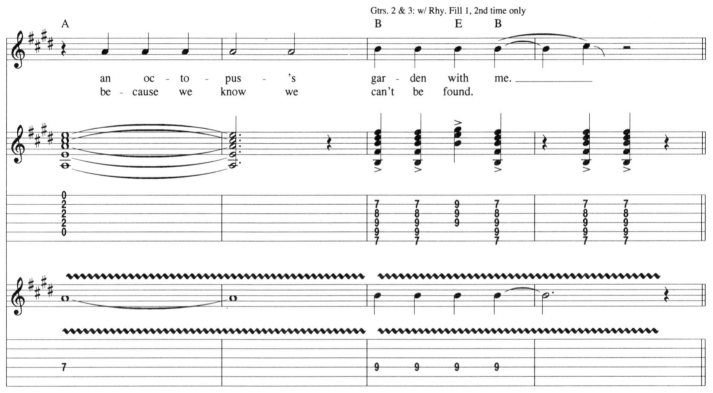

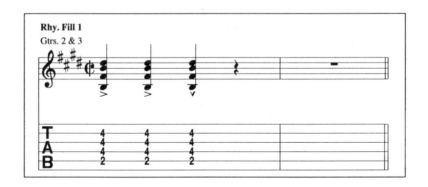

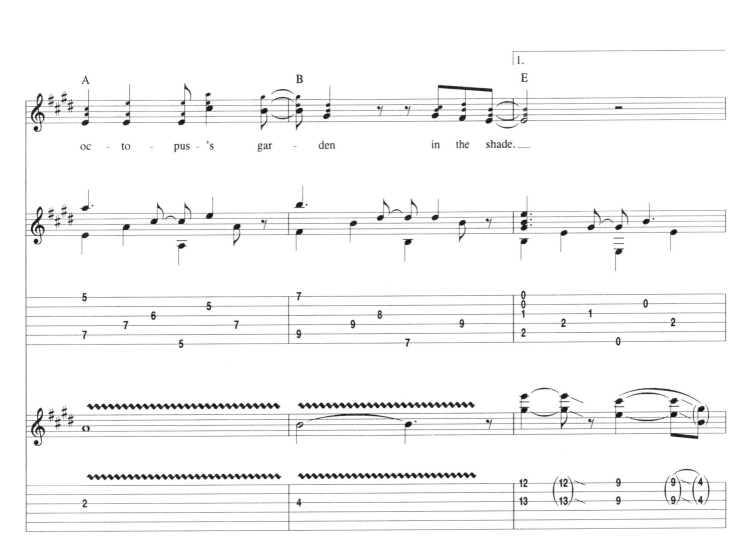

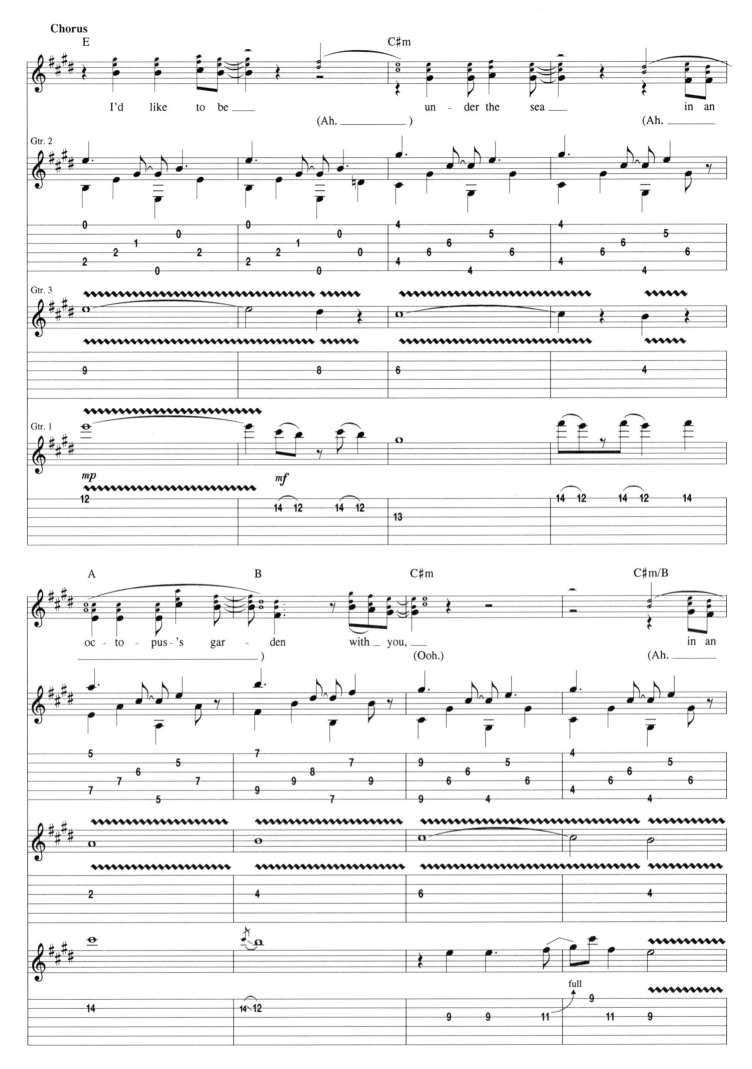

Let It Be

Words and Music by John Lennon and Paul McCartney

Whis - per words ___ of wis - dom, let it be. ___
Oo, oo, oo. _____ Ah.)

D.S. al Coda

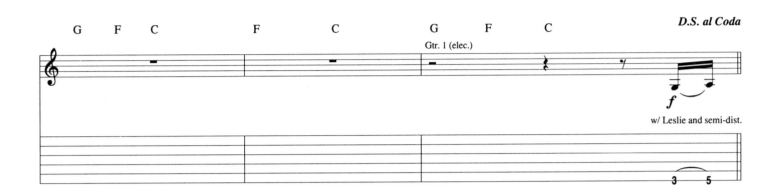

Gtr. 1 (elec.)

w/ Leslie and semi-dist.

⊕ *Coda*

be, ___ hee, ___ ah. Let it be, ___ let it be. Ah, let it be, ___ yeah, let it be. ___
oo, oo. Oo, oo, oo, oo.)

Gtr. 1

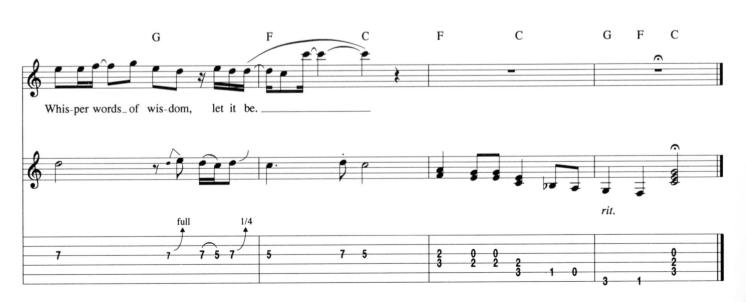

Whis-per words_ of wis-dom, let it be. _____

rit.

Across The Universe

Words and Music by John Lennon and Paul McCartney

G/A G   D

Noth - ing's gon - na change   my world. —

A7   G/A G

Noth - ing's gon - na change   my world. ___   Noth - ing's gon - na change   my world. _

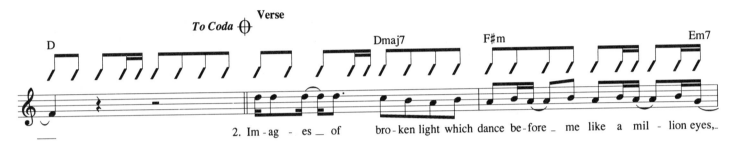

To Coda ⊕ **Verse**

D   Dmaj7   F#m   Em7

___   2. Im - ag - es — of   bro - ken light which dance be-fore — me like a mil - lion eyes,_

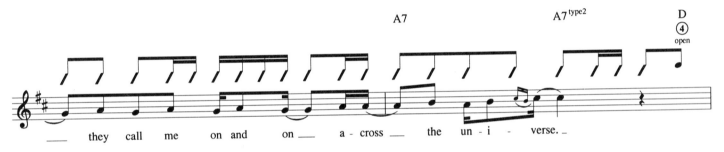

A7   A7 type2   D
④
open

___   they call me   on and   on ___ a - cross ___ the un - i - verse. _

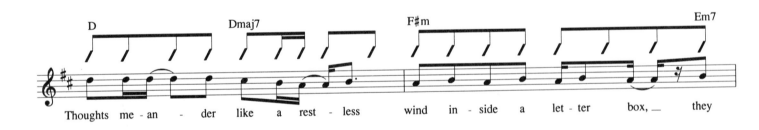

D   Dmaj7   F#m   Em7

Thoughts me - an - der like a rest - less   wind in - side a let - ter box, — they

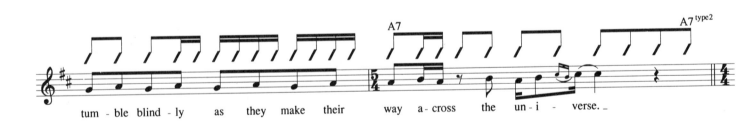

A7   A7 type2

tum - ble blind - ly   as they make their   way a - cross   the un - i - verse. _

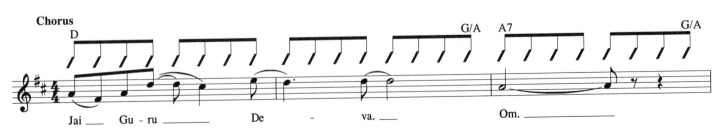

Chorus

D   G/A A7   G/A

Jai ___ Gu - ru ___   De - va. ___   Om.

160

Noth - ing's gon - na change my world. ____ Noth - ing's gon - na change my world. __

Noth - ing's gon - na change my world. __

Noth - ing's gon - na change my world. __ 3. Sounds of laugh - ter, shades of life are

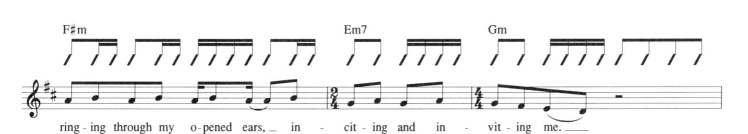

ring - ing through my o - pened ears, __ in - cit - ing and in - vit - ing me. ___

Lim - it - less, __ un - dy - ing love __ which shines a - round __ me like a mil - lion

D. S. al Coda

suns, it calls me on and on ___ a - cross the un - i - verse. __

Jai _____ Gu - ru _____ De - va. _____

161

The Long And Winding Road

Words and Music by John Lennon and Paul McCartney

* Piano and strings arr. for guitar.

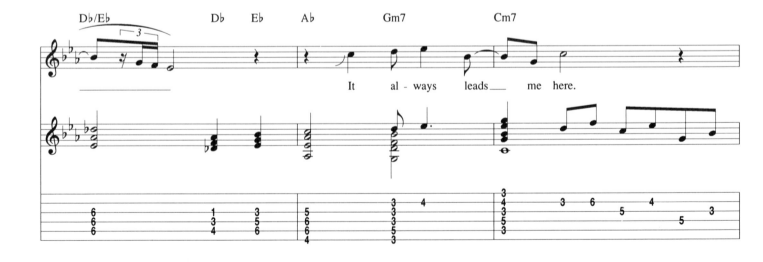

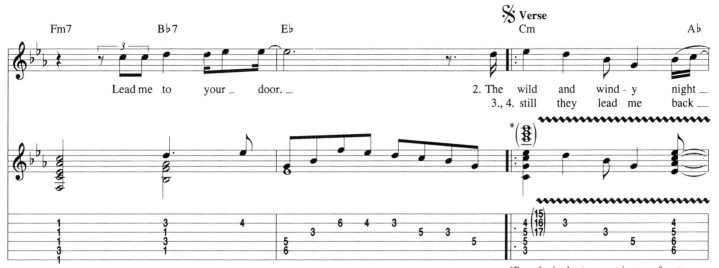

%S Verse

Lead me to your door. ___ 2. The wild and wind-y night ___

3., 4. still they lead me back ___

*Parenthesized notes are strings arr. for gtr.
Play high G second time and full chord on D.S.

Gtr. 2: w/ Fill 1, 1st time

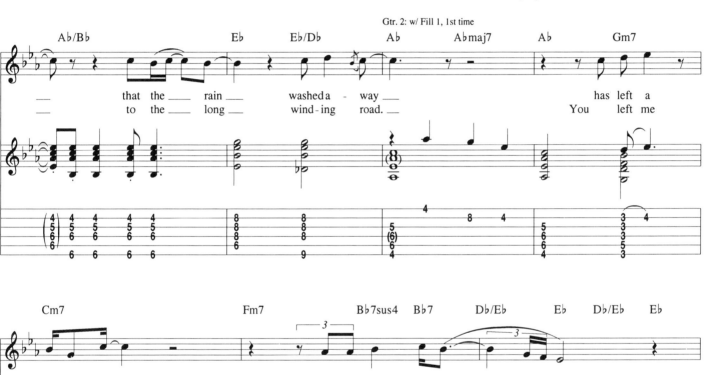

___ that the ___ rain ___ washed a - way

___ to the ___ long ___ wind-ing road. ___ has left a

You left me

pool of tears ___ cry-ing for the day. _____

stand-in' here ___ a long, long time a-go. _____

Fill 1
Gtr. 2 (elec.)

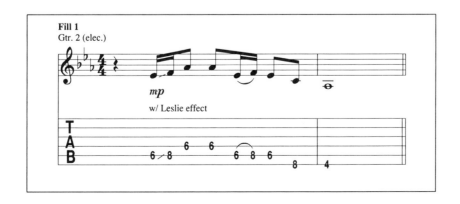

mp
w/ Leslie effect

*Play D 1st time, F 2nd & 3rd times.

**Bass gtr. plays bass notes in slash chord symbols.

*T = Thumb on ⑥

NOTATION LEGEND

Printed in Great Britain by Redwood Books, Trowbridge, Wiltshire

1/98(29728)